COMPLICATED
WATCHES
AND THEIR
REPAIR

COMPLICATED WATCHES
and Their Repair

by

DONALD DE CARLE, F.B.H.I.

Medallist British Horological Institute;
Liveryman, Worshipful Company of Clockmakers;
Chairman, British Horological Institute, 1956–7

Illustrations by

E. A. AYRES, F.B.H.I.

BONANZA BOOKS, NEW YORK

First published serially in
HOROLOGICAL JOURNAL
First impression . . 1956
Facsimile reprint . . 1977

Library of Congress Cataloging in Publication Data
De Carle, Donald.
    Complicated watches and their repair.
    Includes index.
    1. Clocks and watches—Repairing and adjusting.
I. Title.
TS547.D373   1979   681'.114'028   79-13897
ISBN: 0-517-29252-1

PREFACE

Complicated watches have always been interesting to the enthusiastic horologist, but now the need to understand some complicated watches at least has become a daily necessity.

With the increasing production of automatic watches, chronographs and, to a lesser extent, calendar watches, the need to understand such work has become vital.

The aim in this book has been to make the work as straightforward as possible with no ambiguity, and to this end all the illustrations are reproductions of specially made pen and ink drawings.

The predominance given to automatic watches in the book is inevitable for two reasons: one, because there is and will be an ever-increasing number of such watches passing through the workshops for servicing, and, secondly, because there are so many different systems. Whereas modern chronographs and repeaters are fundamentally the same, makers of automatics have revelled in being different from one another.

It may be assumed by some that the repair of complicated watches is difficult, when in fact it is not. It is of course essential for the craftsman to have a sound knowledge and some experience of ordinary watches. Other than this, great care and some thought will ensure success; there are some facts which it is necessary for the beginner in complicated work to be taught and I trust this book will fill that need.

My sincere thanks are due to Mr. E. A. Ayres for his helpful cooperation with such excellent drawings, and to Dr. D. S. Torrens for so carefully reading the proofs of the book. Messrs. Patek Philippe willingly and courteously placed a number of illustrations at my disposal and thanks are especially due to them for the excellent photographs of their perpetual calendar watch which they had made specially for the publisher in order to guide the artist in preparing the dust cover of this book.

My thanks are also due to the many Swiss and American manufacturers who so kindly helped with illustrations and information.

D. de CARLE.

CONTENTS

*If the name of the watch you are looking for does not appear in the above
list the watch may have an Ebauches movement. Compare it with the Bidynator
(Page 7), the Etarotor (Page 16) and the Rotomatic (Page 57).*

Section II : The Chronograph

INTRODUCTION

COMPLICATED work sounds very difficult, but in fact it is not. There are, of course, different degrees of complication in watches, but with experience and the necessary amount of skill, any repairer who works slowly, methodically, accurately, carefully and gently is bound to succeed.

With any complicated work there is one overriding consideration at the work bench—*care*. Complicated watches need much more careful handling than ordinary time-of-day watches. They cannot be repaired in a hurry ; they will not stand it and will eventually get the better of the repairer. Never did the adage " More haste, less speed " more aptly apply.

To become successful repairers of complicated watches students must . be methodical—not that it is unnecessary to be methodical when repairing ordinary watches, far from it—but when dealing with any form of complicated watch it is vital.

Naturally, complicated work should not be the reader's first attempt at watch work and this book is written for the student who is well versed in all ordinary work and knows how to use tools.

The book is concerned with the repair of automatic winding watches ; timers ; chronographs ; split second chronographs ; calendars ; quarter and minute repeaters ; and triple complicated and clock watches. An explanation of the type of watch being dealt with will be given at the beginning of each chapter.

There are numerous versions of the same type of complicated watch. For instance, there are more than 20 different variations of automatic watches and the different types of chronographs must run into dozens. Several different designs or calibres of automatic watch will be considered and one of each of the more popular calibres of chronograph.

Calendar watches (the simple type, and perpetual), repeating watches, and the triple complicated watches which include repeating, chronograph and perpetual calendar mechanisms in the same watch, and clock watches, will receive the attention their importance or popularity calls for.

COMPLICATED WATCHES AND THEIR REPAIR

Section 1

AUTOMATIC WATCHES

This chapter deals with the automatically wound watch with a pedometer form of mechanism. Two types are in common use, one where the rotor makes a complete revolution and the other where the rotor rotates through a segment of a circle and banks on each side upon bumper springs. Of the two systems the one where the rotor makes a complete rotation and winds in both directions is the best. The other system sometimes referred to as the " hammer " type cannot take the fullest advantage of every movement of the wrist of the wearer; further, the constant knocking of the rotor upon the bumper springs can be disturbing to the wearer.

There is little doubt that the automatic watch has come to stay, and the reason is not far to seek. First and foremost is that constant force is supplied by the mainspring during the hours when the watch is worn. Every horologist is conscious of the necessity of a " good action " (i.e., a good arc of vibration of the balance) especially in a watch worn on the wrist. Because of this, the error due to lack of isochronism of the balance is reduced. A good timekeeping rate cannot be expected if the action is poor. By " good rate " is meant a constant error in timekeeping ; for instance, if the rate is, say, 30 seconds per week fast, the watch will not deviate more than a few seconds from that rate either way. It should not suddenly gain or lose, say, 15 seconds on its rate. A watch may keep time to 60 seconds per week but during the week it may be :—

+ 10 the first day ;

+ 30 the second day ;

+ 60 the third day ;

+ 80 the fourth day ;

+ 60 the fifth day ;

+ 40 the sixth day ;

+ 60 the seventh day.

In this case the rate is poor.

A good rate would be + 9 seconds each day. To obtain this condition a watch must reach certain standards—particularly, general good quality in finish, and correct adjustment of the train and the

1

escapement, including the balance and spring. Thirdly, there must be an equal or almost equal torque of the mainspring at all times.

Winding a Watch

To obtain an almost equal torque of the mainspring, a fusee was introduced many years ago, but this practice is not only costly but cumbersome. The next best practice is to use automatic winding.

To obtain the best result from an ordinary winding watch it is necessary to wind it in the morning—or immediately before it is worn—these observations apply particularly to wrist watches. The reason for winding before wearing is to ensure that the balance shall have an arc of, say, $1\frac{3}{4}$ turns. Under these conditions the balance is less liable to be influenced by the movements of the wearer.

Tests have been made indicating that with the slipping mainspring used in automatic watches the torque may not be absolutely constant due to an erratic slipping of the mainspring. When the mainspring is fully wound it may slip back, say, half a turn and with continued use and consequent movement of the rotor, build up again to become fully wound, then slipping back, say, for three-quarters of a turn, and so on.

The variation of torque can, comparatively, be only slight and no doubt a device will be found to correct even this slight error. For instance, eight or more slight notches cut into the inside of the wall of the barrel will prevent a good deal of excessive slipping. But even so, taking the broad view, the automatic winding is still the best, and events have proved it to be so.

Good rates can be obtained with ordinary winding watches and if automatic winding is added to movements of the same size, extraordinarily good rates will be obtained. Manufacturers are inclined to use a small size movement for automatics, say, $9\frac{3}{4}'''$ in a $12'''$ case, to accommodate the automatic mechanism, but there is a trend to use larger movements. Eventually there will be the combination of a large movement and controlled slipping mainspring, which, with the progress already made with balance springs of low thermal error, should produce a watch with almost perfect rate.

Makers of Automatics

A trust, Ebauches S.A., has been formed in Switzerland of the ébauche manufacturers, i.e., the factories which make the framework or major portion of the watch. Other factories make the escapement and there are factories which specialise in making dials, hands, cases, etc. Finally, there are the " finishers." A " finisher " is the factory where the movement from the ébauche factory is completed ; the plates, bridges, etc., are plated and finished ; the movement is jewelled ;

2

escapement fitted ; sprung and timed ; dial and hands fitted and finally the movement cased. There are 17 ébauche factories controlled by Ebauches S.A., but there are dozens of the finishing factories and each of the finishing factories gives the watch it finishes a name, a trade name, and an individuality of its own. In addition there are well over 100 factories in Switzerland that make their own ébauche and finish the movements as well.

Ebauches S.A. factories make three automatic ébauches which are sold to many finishers. The action and repair of these three models are described and also movements of the " complete factories " are dealt with, so that if the reader comes across a movement with a name that is not among the " complete factory " list he will know that it is probably one of the Ebauches movements.

General Notes on Automatics

When winding the watch by the winding button, wind slowly. The automatic winding mechanism terminates in a train of wheels, which are sometimes small with fine pivots, and frequently the wheels are thin and delicate, but quite strong enough for the purpose for which they are normally required. Winding the button vigorously places an undue strain upon these parts mentioned and damage may occur. Some movements are so designed that the train of wheels is not interfered with when winding by the button.

The cost to a manufacturer to tool up and produce a new calibre is enormous, and you may be sure every care has been taken in the design to ensure satisfaction of the finished article. A prototype is made, largely by hand, and thoroughly tested. Each part—wheels, pinions, levers, springs, screws, etc.—is carefully studied as it is in the factory's interest to design and produce the best possible article. Therefore, do not be tempted to alter the design of any part. If you think the fault lies in the malformation of a certain part procure a new piece from the factory that made the movement. It is not advisable to alter the shape of a part or even to repair a damaged part but to fit a new piece as supplied by the manufacturer. It is important to use the mainspring as supplied by the factory. Automatic winding mainsprings are fitted with a special slipping device and although these slipping ends may look simple to make they are not. They are made of a specially-hardened and tempered steel and formed to a required curve. Generally speaking, it is not advisable to remove the mainspring if it looks fresh and clean. Oil the automatic mechanism as indicated. Each manufacturer of the movements described has been approached and the oil and oiling instructions given are those recommended by the actual manufacturer.

3

About Oil

A few words about oil will not be out of place. The viscosity of the oil used in an ordinary watch is important, but it is even more so when dealing with an automatic watch.

The Swiss recommend certain grades for particular parts and invariably they advise Chronax oil, made by Compagnie Française de Raffinage, Paris, France. If this oil is not available an approximate equivalent may be obtained from the table following.

Ragosine watch and clock oils are manufactured by Rocol Ltd., London and Leeds, and have been approved and recommended by Smith's Clocks and Watches, Ltd., being used in all their products :

Chronax Oil	Ragosine Oil
H.H.H.	Grade 300 (a heavy oil).
H.	Grade 180 (chronometers and clocks).
C.	Grade 120 (large watches and small clocks).
D.	Grade 120 (large watches and small clocks).
C.B.A.	Grade 60 (balance holes and escapements of small watches).

Grease

For lubricating some parts where a grease is required, activated grease is recommended. Activated grease is a combination of mineral grease, i.e. petroleum jelly, with the addition of solid animal fat, e.g. stearine or stearic acid, to prevent spreading. Use nine parts petroleum jelly to one part animal fat, well mixed to a fairly stiff paste. The word " active " in this connection means it has non-spreading qualities. Generally speaking, animal (and vegetable, e.g. olive) oils have non-spreading properties, while mineral oils are deficient in that respect, hence an animal or vegetable oil tends to " stay put " while a mineral oil spreads until it dissipates itself away completely from the place where it was originally put. The activation can be achieved in two ways, one by treating the surface to be oiled (Epilame process) and the other by mixing the active substance (animal oil or stearic acid) with the oil. To summarise :

Epilame.—A solution of stearic acid in toluene or carbon tetrachloride or other pure fat solvent. Benzine is not suitable owing to impurities which in course of time have a bad effect on the oil.

Activated (French " activée ") treated to prevent spreading of oil or other lubricant.

Activated lubricant oil or grease containing animal oil or other active substance (e.g. stearic acid, olive oil, neat's-foot oil, etc.).

Activated surfaces.—Surfaces of pivots, jewel holes, etc., which have been treated to prevent oil spreading.

Activated oils are usually petroleum oils to which a certain quantity of animal or vegetable oil has been added.

Activated grease.—Made from a petroleum base, e.g., petroleum jelly with the addition of a solid animal fat such as stearine or stearic acid, or an active oil such as neatsfoot or olive oil.

It might seem that animal or vegetable oil used alone would solve the watchmaker's problems, but this is not practicable as both these types of oil tend to thicken quickly with age and are also subject to considerable thickening at low temperatures. There is one exception to this rule, the oil made by Kelley's from the jaw of the porpoise.

Mineral oil is less likely to become thick with age, and another point in its favour is that, as it is less difficult to refine, its ultimate cost to the watchmaker is less.

The use of a correct oil for a particular purpose is important. If the parts of the automatic mechanism are not oiled with the correct oil the watch may not wind successfully.

Stoppers

When an automatic watch stops and it is not fitted with an " up-and-down " (reserve power) indicator, it is advisable to discover if it is the automatic mechanism or the watch movement which is at fault. If the movement is fitted with up-and-down work it will at once be seen that if the indicator points to fully wound it must be the watch movement that is at fault ; on the other hand, if the indicator points to run down, then it must be the automatic work.

If no indicator mechanism is fitted, it is better to remove the automatic work (or part of it according to the type of movement) and apply the usual tests to the movement to ascertain if it is fully wound. Should it be fully wound, it will be apparent that the fault is with the movement ; but should it not be wound, then the fault is in the automatic work.

It is generally better to assemble the automatic mechanism on to the movement after the movement proper has been fully assembled, with dial and hands, and fitted into its case. When the automatic work has been fitted, apply the following test. (These remarks refer to all movements where a rotor is employed). Hold the watch, sight high, in a vertical position before the back of the case is in place and with the rotor facing you. Now turn the watch, still vertical, so that the rotor falls to the bottom. Keep turning the watch and the rotor should always remain at the bottom. Reverse the direction, and the rotor should still remain at the bottom. If it is found that

5

the rotor lifts and is inclined to rotate with the watch then there is an obstruction. Examine carefully to find where the binding occurs and make the necessary adjustments.

Where bumper springs are employed apply the same test and rotate the watch so that the bumper spring on each side makes contact with the rotor. While this test is being carried out observe that the automatic mechanism is winding the watch.

It is of vital importance that the rotor should be absolutely free, so that the fullest advantage is taken of every movement of the wearer's wrist while the watch is being worn.

The Mainspring

Special care must be given to the mainspring of all automatic winding watches. If it is necessary to remove the mainspring because of thickened oil, clean it carefully with a piece of tissue paper dipped in benzine and draw the spring through a fold, keeping the same curvature of the spring. Do not attempt to straighten out the spring.

Clean the slipping spring device and, before replacing it in the barrel, use activated grease or graphite on the inside wall of the barrel to ensure a steady soft slipping. This is important because if the slipping is jerky it is inclined to let the mainspring slip too much and the amount of slipping controls the amount of force the spring exerts. If the spring slips too much, then the curve of the slipping piece must be flattened out. Conversely, if the spring winds up too tightly it is liable to cause the balance to knock the bankings, and the curve of the slipping piece must be more gentle.

The illustrations Figs. 1 and 2 show the mainspring bridle incorrectly curved, not allowing the mainspring to be fully wound, and correctly curved. These illustrations are intended as a general guide and must not be taken as correct for all watches.

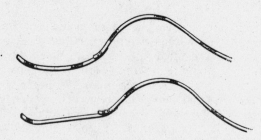

Figs. 1 and 2.—*An incorrect mainspring bridle at top and correctly formed one below.*

Fig. 3 is of a special winder for mainsprings with bridles, made by Bergeon. Practically all Swiss manufacturers recommend this winder.

Some manufacturers of automatic winding watches use the bridle as made and patented by Fabrique Suisse de Ressorts S.A., Fig. 4,

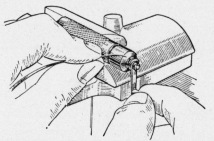

Fig. 3.—*A special mainspring winder by Bergeon for mainsprings with bridles.*

the manufacturers of the Sirius mainspring. The springs, complete with bridle, are supplied in rings and it is advisable to push the spring into the barrel without removing the ring.

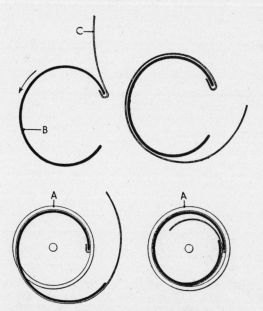

Figs. 4 to 7.—*How a mainspring should be wound by hand. C is the spring, B the bridle and A the barrel.*

If, during repair, it has been necessary to remove the mainspring from the barrel it can be replaced by hand, as shown in the four illustrations Figs. 4 to 7. This method does prevent the risk of damaging the rim of the barrel. If possible, wind the mainspring and bridle into a ring and then present it to and push direct into the barrel. The inside diameter of the ring should be 0.20 to 0.30 mm. larger than the inside diameter of the barrel.

BIDYNATOR (Ebauches, S.A.)

Felsa S.A. Grenchen, Switzerland, make an automatic known as the Bidynator. The size of the movement is $11\frac{1}{2}''' = 26$ mm., calibre No. 690. The rotor traverses through 360°, winding in both directions,

7

and there is a centre seconds hand. Fig. 8 shows the movement, and Fig. 9 shows it with the dial removed.

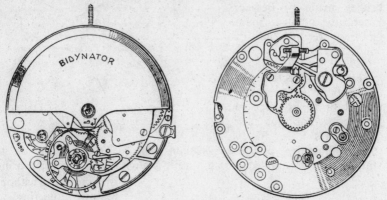

Fig. 8.—*The movement and winding rotor.* Fig. 9.—*The Bidynator with the dial removed.*

To remove the movement from its case, loosen the two screws, *A* and *B* (Fig. 10), and push back the small bolt pieces. Remove the winding shaft and lift the movement out of the case.

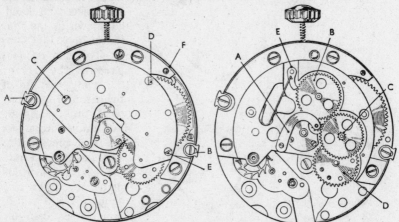

Fig. 10.—*Removing the movement from the case.* Fig. 11.—*The Bidynator showing the automatic winding mechanism, under the plate.*

To take the automatic mechanism to pieces push down the small bolt piece (Fig. 8) to the left as shown by the arrow engraved on the rotor. Lift the rotor straight up, carefully, and away from the movement. It will be noted that there are two jewel holes in the rotor, one fitting on the lower part of the central post, and the other, a smaller hole, for the pivot at the top of the post. If any undue side

8

pressure is brought to bear on the central post while removing the rotor there is a risk of breaking one or both jewel holes, so lift the rotor straight up. It is not necessary to remove the rotor fixing bolt during cleaning, but it is advisable to snap it back into its original position to minimise the risk of the spring jumping out.

Replace the winding shaft and let the mainspring down by holding back the click, which has a slot cut in its upper pivot, F (Fig. 10). Now remove the three screws, C, D, and E (Fig. 10), and lift off the plate, which is the top plate of the automatic work. This will expose the mechanism as shown in Fig. 11.

The action is as follows : The steel wheel fixed to the rotor gears into the small steel wheel which is riveted to the rocking arm, A (Fig. 11), and as the rotor moves, say, to the left, it gears into the steel wheel B, and if to the right, into the steel wheel C, so that as the rotor rotates either to the left or right the wheel C rotates in a clockwise direction. The wheel C has riveted to it a pinion which gears into the wheel D and this last wheel has a ratchet device fitted to a pinion which gears into the main ratchet wheel of the watch movement. If the watch is wound by the winding button the ratchet attached to the pinion of the wheel D rotates backwards so that the train of the automatic mechanism is not reversed.

The click E (Fig. 11) holds the mainspring up during even a small movement of the rotor until sufficient movement has been obtained for the click of the main ratchet wheel to take over. Furthermore, the click E prevents the train from reversing while the strength of the click spring in the wheel D has been overcome during the process of of winding by the button.

Except for the wheel fixed to the rotor, the whole of the automatic work can be taken to pieces for purposes of cleaning. If the rotor needs adjustment because there is too much freedom and a risk of it touching either the inside of the back of the case or the top plate of the movement or there is lack of freedom, thus endangering the winding, it can be corrected by lowering the top jewel hole of the rotor to correct the former fault and by raising it to correct the latter. In either instance it will be necessary to push the hole out and reset it to the required height.

Cut a piece of pegwood so that it fits into the lower hole fairly tightly, then cut the end square so that it will press on the under side of the top jewel hole. Hold the rotor on the pad of the thumb of the left hand and with the pegwood in the right hand slowly and firmly push the top hole out. To reset, use the friction jewel setting tool. (*See* " Practical Watch Repairing," p. 252).

Having cleaned the whole of the movement, reassemble and oil as indicated in the chart (Fig. 12).

Finally apply the tests for freedom of rotor as explained on page 5.

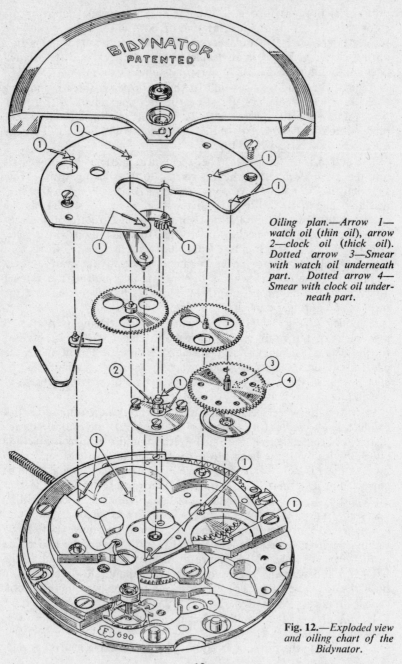

Oiling plan.—Arrow 1—watch oil (thin oil), arrow 2—clock oil (thick oil). Dotted arrow 3—Smear with watch oil underneath part. Dotted arrow 4—Smear with clock oil underneath part.

Fig. 12.—*Exploded view and oiling chart of the Bidynator.*

BOVIMATIC

A pin pallet automatic watch is made by Baumgartner Frëres S.A. Grenchen Switzerland. Known as the Bovimatic B.F.9 Cal. 92 (Fig. 13), it has a very simple and cleverly designed movement. The rotor rotates through a segment of a circle and winds in both directions.

The action is as follows : Fitted to the underside of the rotor is a pin *A* (Fig. 13), which contacts the plate *B*, on to which is fitted a click engaging a ratchet wheel. Another click, *C*, attached to the movement also engages into the same ratchet wheel, *D*. As the rotor revolves to the right the pin in the rotor contacts the plate at *A* in Fig. 14 and pushes it round. The click carried on the plate causes the ratchet wheel to rotate. Fixed to the ratchet wheel is a pinion which gears direct into the main ratchet wheel of the watch. The click fitted on

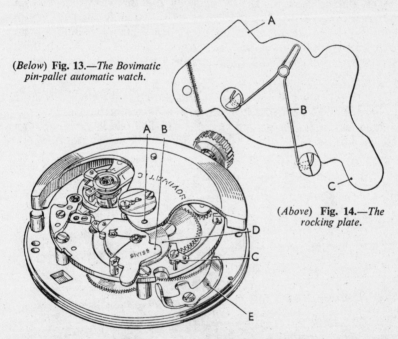

(*Below*) **Fig. 13.**—*The Bovimatic pin-pallet automatic watch.*

(*Above*) **Fig. 14.**—*The rocking plate.*

to the movement holds the mainspring up in position and also acts as the mainspring click. The advantage of this is that the teeth of the ratchet-shaped tooth wheel are fine and in this simple manner the fullest advantage is taken of all movement of the rotor.

The spring *B* (Fig. 14), fitted to the plate, causes it to fly back to its normal position so that the click fitted to the plate idles over the teeth.

As the rotor revolves to the left, the end of the rotor itself contacts the plate at *C* (Fig. 14) and causes it to rotate so that the click again pushes the ratchet wheel round in the same direction, and the click on the movement retains the number of teeth the gathering click has gathered up.

A strong and simple buffer spring stop *E* (Fig. 13) controls the movement of the rotor. The rotor requires a fairly violent shock to cause it to operate, but under test in wear it has proved quite satisfactory. Owing to the necessity of this shock to wind, the normal tests as noted on page 5 issue cannot here be applied.

BULOVA

The Bulova movements are made by the Bulova Watch Co. of America. There are three models ; 10 BPAC and 10 BOAC both with 23 jewels are made in the American factory of Bulova, and 10 CBAC with 17 jewels is made in their Swiss factory. All three models function exactly similarly and the parts are almost completely interchangeable.

The rotor traverses 360° and winds in both directions. Fig. 1 is an exploded view of the automatic winding mechanism and the unique feature is the two crown and castle-like wheels or alternating clutch pinions.

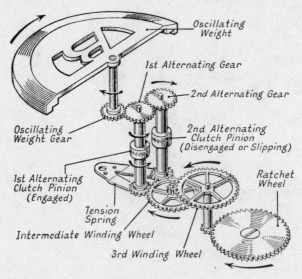

Fig. 15.—*Scheme of the Bulova two-way winding arrangement.*

12

To dismantle, remove the plate, shown in Fig. 16, and lift the rotor up and away from the movement. Then remove the bridge as shown in Fig. 17. Remove the train and tension spring as Fig. 18. The rotor arbor is removed from the automatic winding bridge by taking

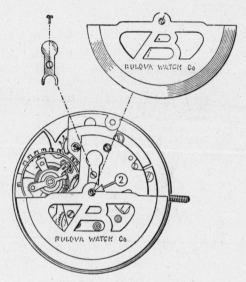

Fig. 16.—*Rotor removed.*

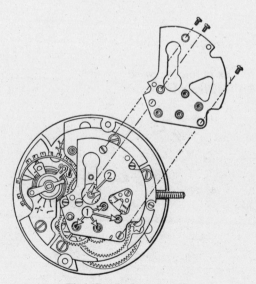

Fig. 17.—*Bridge removed.*

13

off the plate under the bridge, Fig. 19. The movement can now be taken apart in the conventional manner and cleaned.

To re-assemble : assemble the movement up to the automatic work and then proceed in reverse order to that given above. The design is simple and straightforward.

The oiling, as recommended by Bulova, is as indicated by the arrows in Figs. 16, 17 and 18. 1, clock oil ; 2, grease, such as an activated grease.

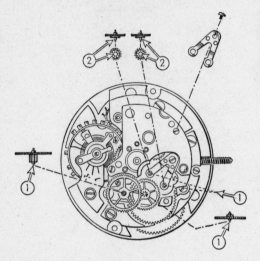

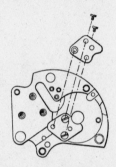

Fig. 18.—*Train and tension spring removed.*   Fig. 19.—*Locking plate removed to release rotor arbor.*

ELGIN

The Elgin automatic is made by Elgin National Watch Co., Elgin, Illinois, U.S.A.

The action of this automatic winding (Fig. 20) is extremely simple. The rotor moves through a segment of a circle, and buffer springs are

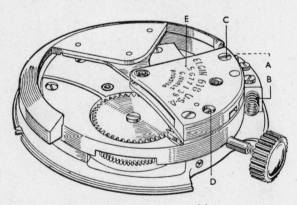

Fig. 20.—*The Elgin automatic.*

14

employed. Attached to the rotor is a segment of a gear which engages another gear segment cut on the end of a rocking arm. Fitted to this rocking arm is a steel ratchet wheel with a pinion fixed to it. The pinion gears directly with the transmission wheel of the keyless mechanism ; a click and spring is fitted to the rocking arm and another and similar click and spring is fitted to the fixed bridge of the auto-wind work. As the rotor oscillates from side to side the rocking arm is caused to move from side to side also, and, by virtue of the click fitted to the arm, the ratchet wheel is made to rotate in one direction. The other small click holds the ratchet in position until the click of the main ratchet wheel takes over.

To dismantle : First remove the two buffer springs, *A* and *B* (Fig. 20), then the two screws *C* and *D*, holding the bridge of the automatic work *E*. The whole of the automatic mechanism can then be lifted off.

Place the automatic work flat on the bench upside down and remove the screw *A* (Fig. 21). The rocking arm *B* can then be removed and also the click *C*. It is not necessary to remove the gear segment from the rotor. Remove the three screws of the plate holding the ratchet wheel on the rocking arm and remove the click.

After cleaning, re-assemble in the following manner : First, the rocking arm—apply a little watch oil to the seating of the ratchet wheel and also to the seating on the plate, then replace the three screws.

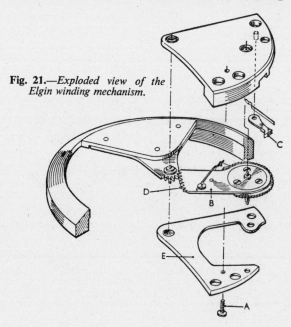

Fig. 21.—Exploded view of the Elgin winding mechanism.

It is of vital importance that this wheel be perfectly free. Replace the click and apply watch oil to the shoulder of the click screw, then fit the click spring. With the bridge *E*, upside down on the bench, place the rotor and the rocking arm in position so that the end tooth of the rocking arm rack engages in the end space of the rotor rack,

15

as *D*. See that the click fitted to the bridge *E* engages with the ratchet wheel; then screw this bridge *E* into position. Oil the lower pivot of the rotor sparingly with watch oil and also oil the lower pivot hole of the rocking arm. Fit the winding stem into the movement. Hold the whole of the automatic assembly firmly with the tweezers and place in position on the barrel bridge.

If the pinion of the rocking arm does not gear immediately with the transmission wheel of the keyless work, just turn the winding button slightly to bring the transmission wheel into its correct position.

Finally, replace the two screws to hold the auto-wind mechanism in position. Oil the upper rotor pivot sparingly with watch oil. The rotor should have no end-shake between its jewel holes, but it must be perfectly free.

Apply the tests as noted on page 5.

ETAROTOR (Ebauches, S.A.)

The next movement is one of which the ébauche is made by Eta S.A. of Grenchen, Switzerland. Figs. 22 and 23 show two views of the movement, one with the dial removed. The name given by the ébauche maker is Etarotor. The size of the movement is $11\frac{1}{2}''' = 25.6$ mm., and the calibre number is 1256. The rotor traverses 360° and it winds the mainspring in both directions. A centre seconds hand is fitted.

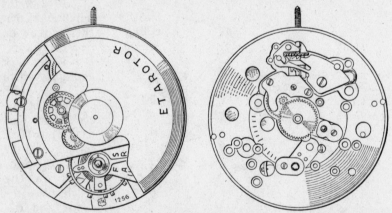

Fig. 22.—*Etarotor automatic winding movement.*   Fig. 23.—*The movement under the dial.*

The movement is removed from its case by first unscrewing the three screws, *A*, *B*, and *C* and removing the automatic device (Fig. 24). This will release the whole of the automatic mechanism. Then remove the winding button and shaft and finally unscrew the two screws, *D* and *E* (Fig. 25) half a turn and the movement can be taken from the case.

The automatic work operates in the following manner. Fixed to the rotor is a steel wheel, *A* (Fig. 26) which gears into two other steel wheels *B* and *C*. Wheel *C* is the reverser wheel and consists of two steel wheels with a plate between them ; they are riveted to a pinion so that the two wheels are free but the plate is fixed to the pinion. On each side of the plate is a small free spring with one end turned up to intercept the arms of the wheels and form a system of click work. The wheel on the rotor gears into one of these wheels and also, as mentioned, into another wheel. Fixed to this last-mentioned wheel, *B*, is another wheel, *D*, with a steel bar between them, and the effect of turning the rotor one way or the other is to cause the plate with the clicks between the two wheels (the reverser) to rotate in one direction only, because

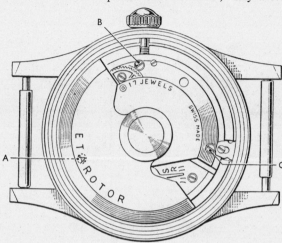

Fig. 24.—*Remove the three screws* A, B *and* C *to release the automatic mechanism.*

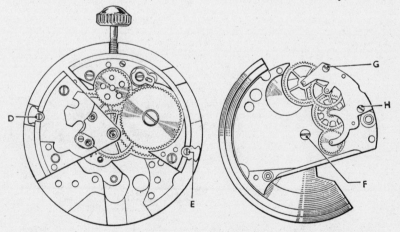

Fig. 25.—*The case fixing screws of the Etarotor movement are shown at* D *and* E.

Fig. 26.—*Dismantling the automatic work of the Etarotor movement.*

17

when one wheel is free-wheeling the other is driving and upon reversing the direction of the rotor the other wheel is driving and the first wheel is free-wheeling.

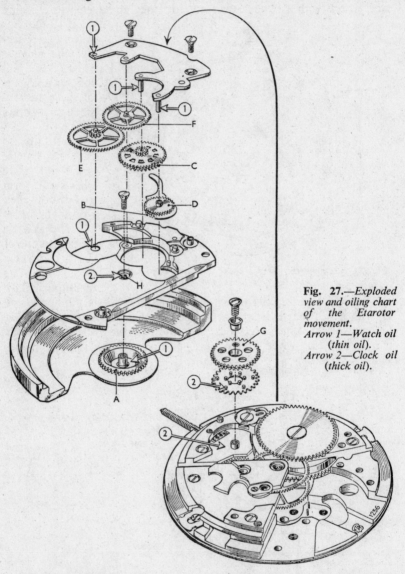

Fig. 27.—*Exploded view and oiling chart of the Etarotor movement. Arrow 1—Watch oil (thin oil). Arrow 2—Clock oil (thick oil).*

The pinion of the reverser wheel attached to the click plate gears into the wheel *E*, which in turn gears into another wheel and pinion,

18

F, which gears into the transmission wheel, *G*, of the ordinary keyless work, and so winds the mainspring.

During repair the reverser wheel is not taken to pieces and neither are the two wheels *B* and *D* riveted to the bar.

To take the automatic work to pieces, unscrew the screw *F* (Fig. 26) which will release the rotor, and then the screws *G* and *H*. Lift off the bridge over the reduction gears, winding pawl and the reverser. The rest of the movement is then taken to pieces and cleaned as explained in " Practical Watch Repairing." The automatic work is cleaned in a similar manner.

Having fully assembled the movement and oiled all the pivot holes in the top plate, fit the movement into the case and proceed to assemble the automatic work. Place the automatic plate on the bench and assemble the wheels. It is not necessary to oil the plate between the reverser wheels or the click work ; it is essential to leave this *perfectly dry*. Give both sides several hard puffs with the bellows to ensure freedom from dust. See oiling chart (Fig. 27) for particulars of oiling and then reassemble the automatic work on to the movement.

If the rotor, through wear, has too much up-and-down shake, it can be reduced in the following manner : Reduce the length of the core *H* (Fig. 27) with a cutter made by whetting the end of an old round file to a pyramid shape at an angle of 60°. Cut very little away at first and try the rotor in position. If the rotor is too tight, adjust the core by raising it a trifle ; place the plate with the core over a hole in a stake and with a small, flat-faced punch, a little smaller than the outside diameter of the core, tap the core up a trifle.

The fitting of the rotor is rather critical ; if it is loose it is liable to rub on the inside of the back of the case, which could cause incorrect operation. On the other hand, if it is too tight it may not operate at all or, if it does move when the watch is worn, it may not move sufficiently to enable the automatic mechanism to wind the main-spring up fully. It is worth spending some time to ensure that the rotor is *accurately free*.

Finally apply the tests for freedom of rotor as explained on page 5.

HELVETIA 837

The Helvetia 837, made by Helvetia Watches, Ltd., Bienne, Switzerland, has an 11½''' movement with centre seconds hand or with off-set seconds hand. (*See* Fig. 28). The rotor revolves through an arc of 360° and winds the mainspring in one direction only.

The action is as follows : fixed to the rotor is a steel pinion which gears into a steel wheel controlled by a pivoted click, so that this wheel can rotate in one direction only. The underside of this wheel has ratchet teeth cut into it and it fits freely on the arbor of another steel wheel, which also has teeth cut into its upper surface, similar to the first wheel mentioned. The two wheels are kept in contact by a spring. The action is similar to that of the crown and castle wheels

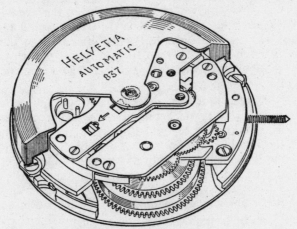

Fig. 28.—*Movement of the Helvetia 837 movement.*

of the conventional keyless mechanism which is known as the Breguet ratchet work. The upper wheel therefore drives the lower wheel in one direction, which in turn gears into another steel wheel with pinion attached, and it is the pinion of the last wheel which gears into a ratchet wheel through a click, driving the ratchet wheel of the mainspring and so winding it up.

When it is required to wind the mainspring manually, two small wheels, which constitute the transmission, come into action. One is pivoted to a small rocking bar, and as the winding button is turned anti-clockwise this wheel is thrown into the lower ratchet wheel, which is the main ratchet wheel and winds the mainspring. Thus during manual winding, the automatic mechanism is not connected at all, and it is necessary to turn the winding button in the reverse direction to the conventional forward direction to wind the mainspring.

To dismantle : withdraw the bolt as indicated by the arrow, and the rotor can be shaken off while holding the bolt back and turning the movement to one side. Hold back the check click A (Fig. 29), so as to release the automatic train and for the main ratchet click to take the power of the mainspring. Remove the two screws B and C and lift off the bridge D, the spring E, the click A and also the wheels F and G. The wheel F is the double ratchet wheel already mentioned. Then remove the screws H and I and the bridge J. Remove the wheel

K and the barrel arbor *L* and the top ratchet wheel with its click and spring, then the ratchet wheel *M* and finally the wheel *N*, and the barrel will slide out from the movement.

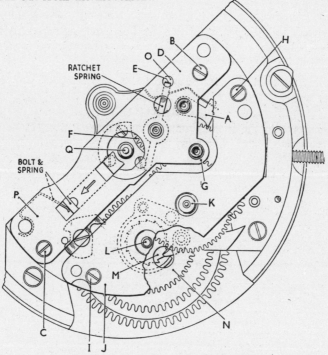

Fig. 29 .—*The Helvetia automatic mechanism.*

Having cleaned the movement and assembled up to the escapement, but not the barrel, start to re-assemble the automatic work. Slide the barrel into position with the steel wheel, then place the ratchet wheel on to the barrel arbor square with the dot marked on it uppermost. Place the ratchet wheel with the click and spring attached over the wheel *M*. First oil with clock oil the click and the spring where it impinges on the click. Now place in position the loose barrel arbor, oiling its bearings first. Oil with watch oil the lower hole of the wheel *K* and place this wheel in position. Replace and screw up the bridge *J*. Oil with watch oil the lower hole of the wheel *F* and *G*, and apply clock oil to the ratchet teeth between the two wheels of *F*. Place this wheel and the wheel *G* in position, and also the click *A* and then the spring *E*. See that the turn-up end is uppermost and in position so that the turn-up end will enter into the hole *O*. Apply a little watch oil under the spring first. The bolt and its spring can be placed into position later.

21

Now replace the bridge *P*. Unscrew the screw *C* and lift up the end of the bridge *P* to allow the spring and bolt to be slipped under and into position, and then screw down the bridge.

Apply clock oil to the post *Q*, and also to the groove above the wheel fixed to the rotor. Hold the bolt back as indicated by the arrow, place the rotor into position and release the bolt. Oil with watch oil the top pivots of the automatic train.

Apply the tests as noted on page 5.

INTERNATIONAL

The rotor of the International automatic movement, made by the International Watch Company, Schaffhausen, Switzerland, revolves the complete circle and winds in both directions, Fig. 30.

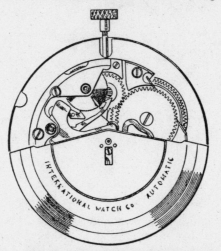

Fig. 30.—*The International automatic.*

The action is as follows : Fixed to the rotor is the heart-piece *A*, Fig. 31, and as the rotor rotates, it moves the rocking arm *B*, which is pivoted at *C*, through the two rollers *D* and *E*. The rocking arm consists of two plates and the rollers and the two clicks *F* and *G* are pivoted between the plates. As the rotor moves to the right the heart-piece in turn moves the roller *E* upwards, and the click *G* idles over the ratchet teeth of the wheel *H*. At the same time the click *F* draws the wheel *H* round to the left. Conversely, as the rotor moves to the left, it moves the rocking arm downwards and the click *F* then idles and the click *G* draws the wheel *H* to the left. Fixed to the wheel *H* is a pinion which gears into the transmission wheel of the watch movement and so winds the mainspring.

22

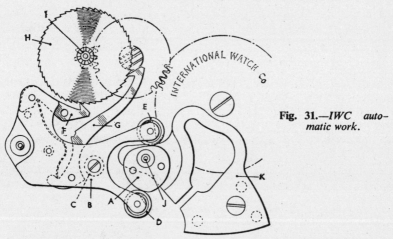

Fig. 31.—*IWC auto-matic work.*

It is a simple and most ingenious system, well constructed and beautifully finished.

The rotor is pivoted on to the post *J* which is fixed to the substantial shock-absorbing spring *K*. The mainspring is the slipping variety, employing the system as illustrated in Figs. 4 to 7.

To dismantle, first remove the rotor. To do this, unscrew the screw in the centre half a turn and pull back the small bolt-piece. The rotor can then be lifted off.

The tension of the mainspring held by the clicks is relieved by pressing the click *A* (Fig. 32) back until it is locked in the notch *B* of the click *C*. This movement disengages the click *C* from the wheel *D*. The full power of the mainspring is then let down in the con-

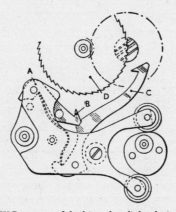

Fig. 32.—*IWC system of locking the clicks during dismantling.*

ventional manner by holding the winding button and withdrawing the click from the main ratchet wheel. This system is useful when fitting a new mainspring. It is then only necessary to remove the rotor and its support *K* (Fig. 31).

To proceed with the dismantling, remove the two screws holding the automatic mechanism bridge. The ratchet-toothed wheel and the rocking arm can then be removed. Next, remove the rotor support. The rocking arm assembly is dismantled by removing the screw holding the upper plate. It is not necessary to remove the heartpiece from the rotor.

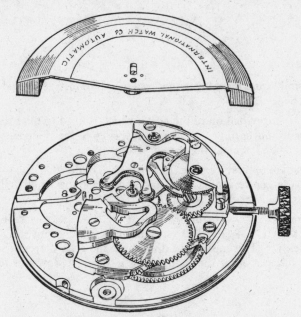

Fig. 33.—*The IWC automatic bridge is held by two screws.*

Re-assembly

Clean the movement and assemble it up to the automatic work. Having cleaned the parts of the automatic work, assemble as follows : Re-assemble the rocking arm and oil the bearings of the rollers and the clicks and also the points where the spring of the clicks contacts the clicks with very little clock oil before replacing the upper plate. Apply clock oil to the lower pivot holes of the ratchet-toothed wheel and the rocking arm. Replace the rotor post spring. Apply clock oil very sparingly to the levers of the ratchet-toothed wheel and then place this wheel and the rocking arm assembly in position, and finally screw on the automatic mechanism bridge. Oil the top pivots of the ratchet-toothed wheel and the rocking arm. With clock oil, oil the post for the rotor and screw the rotor back into position. Apply very little clock oil to the nose of both clicks operating on the ratchet-toothed wheel and just smear to the edge of the heart-piece of the rotor. The oiling chart is shown in Fig. 34. Now apply the tests as noted on page 5.

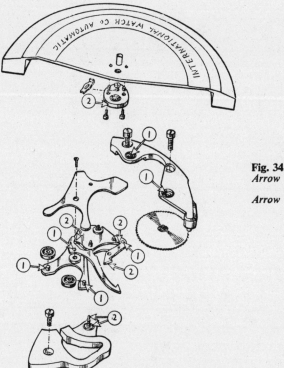

Fig. 34.—*IWC oiling chart. Arrow 1—Watch oil (thin oil). Arrow 2—Clock oil (thick oil).*

LECOULTRE

LeCoultre, of Le Sentier, Switzerland, make three models of automatic-winding watches : Calibres 497, 476, and 481. Cal. 481 and 476 employ similar automatic mechanism. Cal. 497 is the latest model and the one described.

The movement of Cal. 497 is a departure from the conventional automatic-winding watch inasmuch as the rotor is arrested when the mainspring is fully wound and the slipping mainspring device is not necessary. No provision is made to wind the watch manually ;

a few shakes of the watch are sufficient to start the balance vibrating at a good amplitude; since the mainspring is set up before winding starts, it is virtually fitted with stop work. It is interesting to note that this system is, fundamentally, the same as that employed by Recordon, who was granted a patent in 1780 in England.

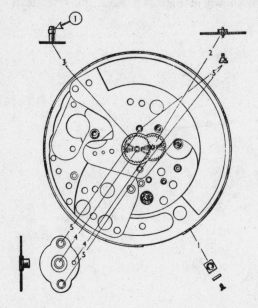

Fig. 35.—*The LeCoultre automatic. The numerals, continued to Fig. 39, indicate the order of assembly. The arrows indicate oiling points.*
Arrow 1—Watch oil (thin oil).
Arrow 2—Clock oil (thick oil).

The rotor operates through a segment of a circle and winds in both directions. The buffer springs are shown in Fig. 38, No. 27.

The movement is 12‴ and a 12‴ escapement is employed. The action is as follows : Screwed to the under-side of the rotor is the plate *A* (Fig. 38), which has fixed to it the steel wheel *B*. This wheel, with another wheel of similar size, is pivoted on to a small rocking arm, and, as the rotor moves backward and forward, one or other of these two wheels is made to gear into the wheel *C*, which has ratchet-shaped teeth. As wheel *C* is made to rotate it is held up by the click and spring combined *D*. It is this click which holds up the mainspring ; there is no click work associated with the main ratchet wheel.

Fixed to the wheel *C* is a pinion gearing into the transmission wheel, which in turn, through a pinion, gears into the ratchet wheel to wind the mainspring.

The barrel arbor has a long left-hand thread, on to which is screwed a disc. Two long-headed screws are screwed into the barrel cover and the disc, which has holes drilled into it, and is able to rise as the barrel arbor is turned during winding and to fall as the barrel rotates, because the two screws already mentioned will cause the disc to rotate.

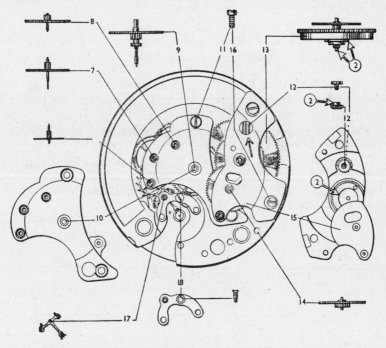

Fig. 36.—*Parts and order of assembly of the LeCoultre automatic.*

Attached to the lever E (Fig. 66) is a cone-shaped stud, and this stud is made to bear upon the periphery of the steel disc ; therefore, as the disc rises it pushes the lever to one side, and when the disc has reached its highest position, i.e. when the mainspring is fully wound, the pin on the lever E will contact the hook (Fig. 38).

This spring hook is fixed to the under plate of the rotor, and therefore the rotor is arrested. As the disc is lowered by the running of the watch, so the pin disengages the hook and the rotor is then free to rotate—an ingenious device which is in principle the same as that employed in the earliest automatic-winding watches already mentioned.

Up-and-Down Work

The rack G (Fig. 38) is controlled by the lever E, and this gears into the pinion H which is fitted with a pipe on to which the up-and-down hand is fitted.

27

This watch seems a little more complicated than some automatic watches, but it is, in fact, quite simple. Care is needed in dismantling and assembling, and LeCoultre suggest the order as numbered in Figs. 35 to 39.

To Dismantle

These instructions apply only to dismantling and assembling the automatic work. First let down the power of the mainspring. The screw A (Fig. 39) has fixed to it a small wheel which gears with the ratchet wheel. The sole purpose of this wheel is to let down the mainspring. There is no winding shaft.

Place the properly-shaped blade of a screwdriver in the slot and carefully and firmly turn clockwise, at the same time holding back the click, through the hole B (Fig. 39). Then slowly let the screwdriver revolve to let down the spring (4 turns of the screw = 1 turn of the barrel arbor). N.B. : The screw A and the thread of the barrel arbor for the disc are left hand.

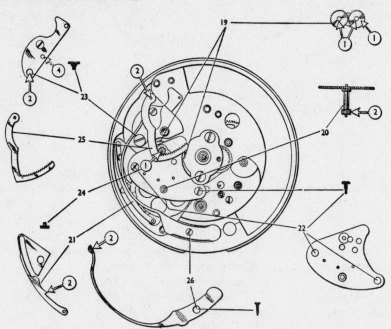

Fig. 37.—*LeCoultre automatic parts shown for assembly and oiling.*

The numbers (not those in circles) given in Figs. 35 to 39 indicate the order of assembly, therefore, to dismantle, start at the last number 33. The two screws marked $E1$ and $E2$ (Fig. 38) are eccentric screws and should not be touched. They are used for the adjustment of the up-and-down work and for the correct position for the arresting hook of the rotor.

Having taken the movement to pieces, next deal with the barrel. Holding the barrel arbor by its square, in the pin tongs, wind up the mainspring a fraction of a turn and hold the barrel ; then remove the two screws holding the disc and unscrew the disc—left hand thread. The barrel, etc., is cleaned in the conventional manner.

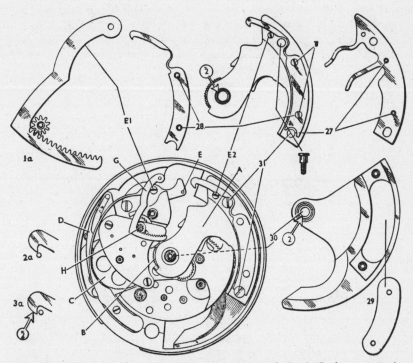

Fig. 38.—*Parts order of assembly and oiling points of the LeCoultre automatic watch. Part 1a shows the up-and-down rack.*

To assemble the barrel, hold the arbor in the pin tongs as before and wind the mainspring up to 1 to $1\frac{1}{4}$ turns, screw the disc hard on to the arbor, and replace the two screws (Fig. 40). The mainspring is thus set up. Having cleaned the movement and assembled up to number 18 (Fig. 36), proceed to assemble the automatic work as Figs. 37 to 39. Oiling points other than pivots are noted in the illustrations by numbers in circles. Oil with moderation. The pivots are oiled in the conventional manner with watch oil.

Having assembled the movement, the adjustments to observe are : With the mainspring run down (to the limit of the stop work), see that the up-and-down rack is in the position shown in 1*a* (Fig. 38), i.e. just resting on the eccentric screw-head, allowing the pinion for the up-and-down hand to be placed in position. Next, wind the mainspring up three turns (12 turns of the screw *A*, Fig. 39), and the hook of the rotor should be as 2*a* (Fig. 38) with relation to the pin, that is to say, it should just pass the pin. Wind the screw *A* (Fig. 39) four more turns (1 turn of the barrel arbor) and the hook should engage the pin as the figure under 2*a* (Fig. 38). Make sure the hold is secure so that a sudden shock will not release the rotor.

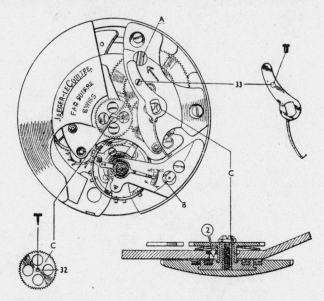

Fig. 39.—*LeCoultre automatic, showing the hand setting mechanism, the screw to let down the mainspring* (A) *and the click spring* (B).

The up-and-down hand is placed in the zero position when the mainspring is down.

The hands are set by sliding the button on the back of the case to one side : towards the centre of the case to set the hands and towards the edge of the case for the neutral position. When this button is moved to the hands set position the lever into which the head of wheel *C* fits is moved to stop the balance.

The wheel *C* (Fig. 39) is for the purpose of setting the hands.

Apply the tests as noted on page 5.

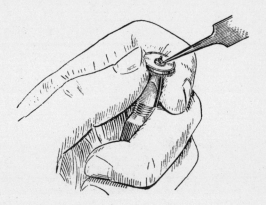

Fig. 40.—*Setting up the LeCoultre mainspring.*

LEMANIA

Made by Lemania Lugrin, S.A. Orient, Switzerland, the Lemania movement is 12 ligne in size. The calibre number is 3,600. The rotor oscillates 360°, winding in one direction only. Fig. 41 shows the movement.

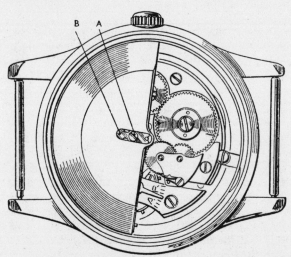

Fig. 41.—*Movement of the Lemania automatic which winds through 360 degrees.*

The action is as follows : The rotor has fitted to it a steel pinion which is free to rotate, a long side click and spring combined allows it to revolve in one direction only and it is this spring which conveys the driving force to wind the main spring. This pinion gears into a brass wheel *A* (Fig. 42), which is controlled by a wire click *B* ; this wheel has a pinion attached to it which in turn gears into another wheel *C*. The wheel *C* has a pinion attached to it which gears into the upper of

31

two ratchet wheels of exactly the same size *D*. Both the upper and lower ratchet wheels have round holes. The top surface of the lower wheel has notches cut into it and the upper ratchet wheel has similar notches cut into its under-surface. The double three-pronged spring *E* (Fig. 43) is squared on to the barrel arbor and operates between the ratchet wheels.

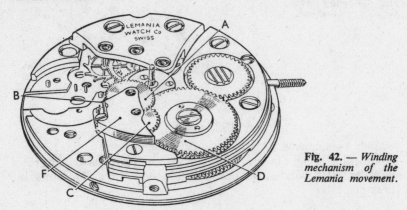

Fig. 42. — *Winding mechanism of the Lemania movement.*

As the top ratchet wheel rotates through the operation of the rotor, the notches in the under-side of the ratchet contact the three-pronged spring and cause the mainspring to wind and the wire click *B* to act as a ratchet click, until the click of the main ratchet wheel takes over.

When the watch is wound by hand the lower ratchet is made to rotate in the conventional manner and the notches in that wheel contact the three-pronged spring and so the mainspring is wound without interfering with the automatic mechanism. To dismantle the automatic work, remove the screw *A* (Fig. 41), and withdraw the steel plate *B*. The rotor can then be lifted up off the centre post and away from the movement. Next, let the mainspring down by holding back the wire click *B* (Fig. 42). The main click of the mainspring ratchet wheel then holds the mainspring up and this can be let down in the usual manner. Remove the bridge *F*, and then the two wheels. Remove the ratchet wheel screw and lift off the top ratchet wheel, the three-pronged spring and then the lower ratchet wheel.

When re-assembling particular attention must be given to the freedom of the two ratchet wheels, and satisfy yourself that the three-pronged spring is operating correctly in the rectangular sinks or notches without excessive tension. For correct oiling refer to oil chart (Fig. 43). Apply the tests noted on page 5. This movement is of sturdy construction and the design is most simple and highly efficient.

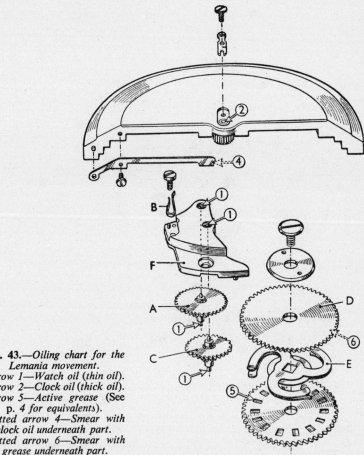

Fig. 43.—*Oiling chart for the Lemania movement.*
Arrow 1—Watch oil (thin oil).
Arrow 2—Clock oil (thick oil).
Arrow 5—Active grease (See p. 4 for equivalents).
Dotted arrow 4—Smear with clock oil underneath part.
Dotted arrow 6—Smear with grease underneath part.

LONGINES

Made by the Longines Watch Co., St. Imier, Switzerland, and known as calibre 22A, the rotor of the Longines automatic revolves through 360° and winds both ways.

First remove the movement from its case by releasing the winding button and shaft, then loosen the two screws holding the movement in its case. Unscrew the screw *A* (Fig. 44), and withdraw the fork piece. Hold back slightly the rocking arm *C* (Fig. 45) and lift the rotor straight up and off its post. The automatic work operates as follows : fixed to the rotor is a heart-shaped piece ; a steel roller is fitted to the rocking arm by a shouldered screw, which is held towards the heart piece by

33

a spring so that as the rotor revolves in either direction the rocking arm, pivoted at *A* (Fig. 45) is made to swing in and out.

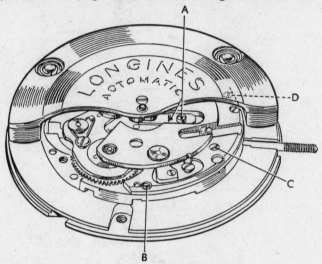

Fig. 44.—*Longines movement.*
A—*screw retaining rotor.* B C D *screws retaining top plate of automatic work.*

The underside of the rocking arm (Fig. 45) has fitted to it the steel wheel and pinion *B* ; gearing into the larger wheel is the small steel wheel which is located in an oval hole ; the wheel is shoulder-screwed on to a disc and this carriage is kept in contact with the steel plate *D* by a spring. The steel plate *D* has a milled edge D^1, and as the small wheel rotates in an anti-clockwise direction it passes the milled edge (disengaging), but when reversed the teeth of the milled edge lock it, so that this wheel and consequently the larger wheel can rotate in one direction only ; the milled edge and the smaller wheel act as a fine click. The large wheel also gears into the steel wheel *E*, which is

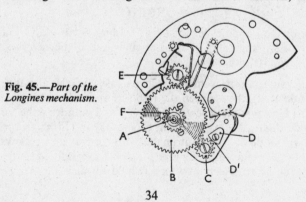

Fig. 45.—*Part of the Longines mechanism.*

34

located in an oval hole and is controlled by a steel plate with a milled edge, similar to the plate *D*. As the large wheel rotates in a clockwise direction both the small wheels rotate anti-clockwise and are free to pass the milled edge, but are locked when reversed ; we shall see the object of this presently. The pinion *F* gears direct into the main ratchet wheel. As the rotor rotates backwards or forwards the wheel *B* is made always to advance by virtue of the locked wheel *C*. The wheel *E* acts as a fine click, so that advantage is taken of the slightest movement of the rotor and this wheel holds up the mainspring until the ratchet click takes over.

To resume taking the automatic work to pieces : having removed the rotor spring *A* (Fig. 44), remove the three screws *B, C, D*, and take off the top plate of the automatic work. Now remove the rocking arm and unscrew the steel roller and the two wheels. Unscrew the wheel from the underside of the plate. It is not necessary to remove the two steel plates with the milled edges, and it is not necessary to dismantle the rotor. It will be noted that the weight of the rotor is held to the segment by studs and springs. The object of this is that these springs take any violent shock and so prevent damage to the centre pivoting. The springs are so designed that they act as shock-absorbers both in the horizontal and vertical directions. Having cleaned the movement and the automatic work, re-assemble the automatic last after the movement has been fitted into its case.

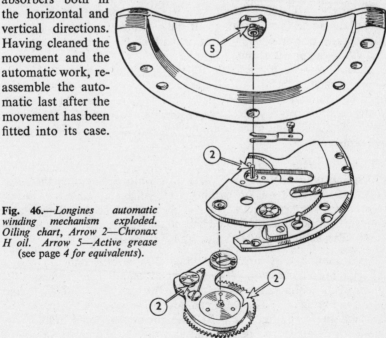

Fig. 46.—*Longines automatic winding mechanism exploded. Oiling chart, Arrow 2—Chronax H oil. Arrow 5—Active grease (see page 4 for equivalents).*

Messrs. Longines give special instructions about oiling. They recommend Chronax H for the light oiling and HHH for the heavy. Grease the interior of the mainspring barrel with graphite before winding in the mainspring. This enables the slipping hook to slide round without jerking. Before assembling the barrel into the movement check the mainspring action (*see* page 6). Refer to the oiling chart for the correct method of oiling (Fig. 46).

It is essential that all moving parts of the automatic work should be perfectly free. Apply the test for freedom of rotor as mentioned on page 5. This movement is well designed and beautifully finished.

MOVADO

The Movado Factories, La Chaux-de-Fonds, Switzerland, make two automatic models, both of the same size, but working on different principles. Each is fitted with a rotor making a part revolution and banking upon buffer springs and they each wind in one direction only. One model is Calibre 331, which Movado claim to be the flattest automatic yet made, and the other Calibre 221, also known as the Tempomatic.

Dealing with Calibre 331 first, in Fig. 47, the rotor consists of a steel plate cut to form a spring. If the watch receives a shock either horizontally or vertically, the spring part of the rotor arm gives so that the centre pivots of the rotor working in jewelled holes are relieved of shock. Riveted to the outer edge of the rotor is a band of heavy metal. Fixed to the arbor of the rotor is a steel pinion which engages with the teeth cut into the end of a brass rocking arm. Mounted on to the rocking arm is a steel fine-toothed ratchet wheel with pinion attached and this pinion gears into the transmission wheel of the keyless mechanism.

Fitted on to the rocking arm is a click and spring and a similar click and spring is fitted to the top plate of the movement. As the rotor oscillates, the click on the rocking arm gathers up the teeth of the fine-toothed ratchet wheel and the click fitted to the top plate retains the wheel in position until the click of the main ratchet wheel takes over. The action is quite simple and well designed.

To dismantle, first turn the winding shaft a little and draw back the retaining click *A*, Fig. 47, so that the automatic work is free of the power of the mainspring. Then remove the three screws *B*, *C*, *D*, and lift off the bridge *E*. The rotor can now be removed, also the rocking arm and the retaining click. Remove the three screws holding the fine-toothed ratchet in position and also the gathering click *F*.

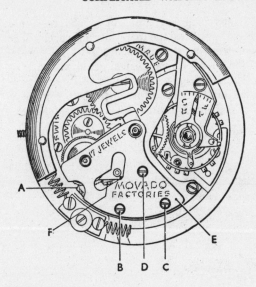

Fig. 47.—*The Movado Calibre 331.*

Re-Assembly

After cleaning in the conventional manner the whole movement, including the automatic work, and having re-assembled the movement, proceed to assemble the automatic mechanism. Movado recommend lubricating the mainspring and the slipping bridle with graphite grease —a mixture containing 1 to 2 per cent. graphite. Oil the seating of the fine-toothed ratchet wheel with clock oil and replace the three screws. Fit the gathering click and also the retaining click into position and apply a little clock oil to their bearings. Oil the lower pivot holes of the rocking arm and the rotor with clock oil. Place the rotor in position and then the rocking arm. Arrange so that when the rotor is midway between the buffer springs the pinion leaves engage in the teeth in the centre of the rack of the rocking arm. This is important, to ensure that the leaves of the pinion in the rotor engage the rocking arm teeth during a complete swing of the rotor.

Oil the upper pivots of the rocking arm and the rotor with clock oil. Apply clock oil sparingly to the teeth of the fine-toothed ratchet wheel and work the rotor to and fro so that the oil is picked up by the noses of the gathering and retaining clicks. Finally, apply the tests as enumerated on page 5.

The other movement is Calibre 221, aso known as Movado Tempomatic, Fig. 48. The rotor is of similar design to Calibre 331, but without the spring device. Fitted to the rotor is a gathering click and spring, *A*, Fig. 48. Pivoted under the plate *B* are four steel wheels with a retaining click engaging into the second wheel.

37

The fourth and last wheel has fixed to it a pinion which gears into the wheel fitted to the barrel arbor above the main ratchet wheel. The main ratchet wheel is squared on to the barrel arbor in the normal manner, and on the top of the wheel is a small steel wheel with ratchet shaped teeth. The top wheel C, Fig. 48, has fitted to its underside a click and spring. It has a round hole and fits on to the top pivot of the barrel arbor. This wheel is held in position by a washer and screw.

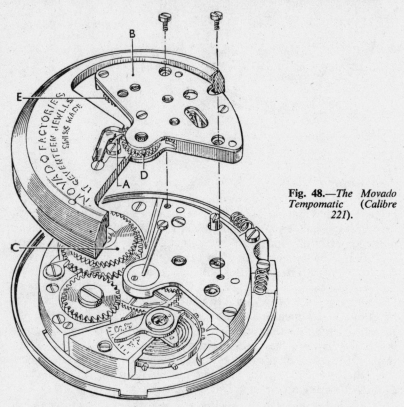

Fig. 48.—*The Movado Tempomatic (Calibre 221).*

The action is as follows : As the rotor oscillates backwards and forwards the click A, Fig. 48, gathers up the wheel D which transmits to the next wheel ; this last-mentioned wheel is controlled by a retaining click and spring holding up the automatic train until the click of the main ratchet wheel takes over. The pinion of the last wheel causes the wheel C to rotate and through its click the ratchet wheel is made to rotate and so the mainspring is wound.

If the watch is wound manually, the main ratchet wheel is made to rotate and the click fitted to the wheel C idles over the teeth of its ratchet wheel, and the train of the automatic work is not interfered with at all. It is a simple, clever, and well-designed movement. The oiling instructions recommended by Movado are similar to those given for Calibre 331. The click between the two ratchet wheels is oiled with clock oil and also the surface of the upper wheel where it contacts the small ratchet wheel. Apply a little clock oil to the undersurface of the washer. Finally apply the test as noted on page 5.

OMEGA

Made by Omega Watch Co., Bienne, Switzerland, the Omega automatic has a basic reference number of 342, Fig. 49. Other numbers may be found in some models and these additional numbers refer to alterations or modifications (height of hands, etc.), where they differ from standard.

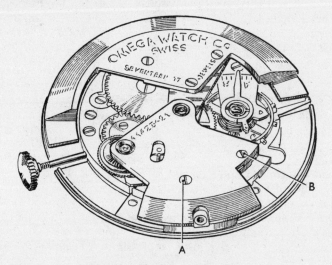

Fig. 49.—*The Omega automatic.*

The rotor oscillates through a segment of a circle and bumper springs are employed. The winding operations as the rotor moves in one direction only. The automatic winding functions in the following manner : Fixed to the rotor is a steel plate with pivoted arbor. On the end of this plate are cut seven teeth which engage with the teeth cut on the end of the rocking arm. Fitted to the rocking arm and free to rotate is a ratchet wheel and with this two clicks engage, one fitted to the rocking arm and the other to the top plate of the watch movement. Fixed to the ratchet wheel is a pinion which gears into the transmission wheel of the keyless work. As the rotor swings backwards and forwards, the arm rocks from side to side and the click attached to it gathers up the teeth of the ratchet to move it forward. The click fitted to the top plate of the movement holds the ratchet wheel in position until the main ratchet wheel of the mainspring takes over. The design is very simple and sturdy and the execution of a high order.

To dismantle, first release the click fitted to the rocking arm by inserting a fine point in the hole of the auto-wind bridge, where the pin fixed to the click can be seen. If the click is moved far enough back its spring will hold it there, free of the fine-toothed ratchet wheel. While in this state let the mainspring down in the conventional manner, as explained in " Practical Watch Repairing." The two screws, *A* and *B*, Fig. 49 can now be removed. Lift off the bridge of the automatic work and then the rotor and the rocking arm. Remove the click from the rocking arm, and unscrew the fine-toothed ratchet wheel. Remove the click from the top plate. The automatic winding parts are cleaned in the conventional manner, and before describing re-assembly here are a few observations about the mainspring by the Omega Watch Co.

The slipping device is as shown in Fig. 49. If it is found necessary to remove the mainspring because of thick oil, etc., clean both the spring and attachment by drawing them through a piece of rag, holding the spring between the points of tweezers, *without causing deformation*. The spring should not be washed in any liquid. The slipping attachment is cleaned in a similar manner. Before replacing the slipping attachment and mainspring pass them in the fold of an oily rag, holding the spring as before, so as to apply a thin film of oil to both sides of the spring and the attachment. Use the special winder to insert the attachment and spring, as noted in the remarks on page 7. When the arbor and cover have been assembled check that the spring can be wound at least five turns before slipping occurs.

Before barrels are passed in the factory they must give $5\frac{1}{2}$ turns before slipping. One should barely be able to feel the slipping occur if the action of the attachment is correct. If the desired result is not obtained, remove the mainspring and attachment. Check the outer surface of the attachment for smoothness. If necessary, open out the slipping attachment so that it will grip the inside of the barrel harder. If there is any doubt about the attachment do not hesitate to change it and if slipping persists, thicker attachments are available.

Now to re-assemble the automatic work : When all the parts have been inspected and found to be in good condition and perfectly clean they are lubricated. The points listed below should be oiled with a relatively thick oil (Moebius No. 1 chronometer oil). Use an exceedingly small quantity, just sufficient to form a very thin film :—

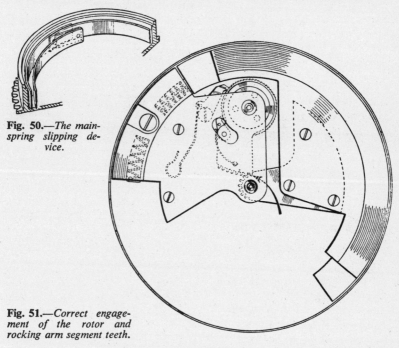

Fig. 50.—*The mainspring slipping device.*

Fig. 51.—*Correct engagement of the rotor and rocking arm segment teeth.*

The bearings of the two clicks, one on the rocking arm and the other on the top plate. The ends that operate on the ratchet teeth and also where the springs bear on to the clicks. The teeth of the transmission wheel. The fine teeth of the ratchet wheel. The teeth on the rocking arm and also the teeth on the rotor. The bearing surfaces of the fine tooth ratchet wheel in the rocking arm. The pivots of the rocking arm and the rotor are oiled in the conventional manner. Watchmakers may hesitate to oil the teeth of wheels, but this procedure is recommended by the Omega Watch Co. and such advice could with advantage be applied to other makes of watches with a similar system of automatic mechanism.

The buffer springs should be wiped over with an oily rag to ensure that their entire outer surface is sufficiently lubricated so as to minimise the effects of rubbing.

See that the two clicks are perfectly free and that they do not have excessive end-shake, to ensure that they engage with the fine-tooth ratchet correctly. See that the click springs engage in the grooves formed in the clicks.

Oil the lower pivot hole of the rocking arm, place it in position, then oil the lower pivot hole of the rotor. Arrange so that the last tooth of the rotor segment engages in the last space of the rocking arm segment, Fig. 51. This is essential as it ensures that the rotor will traverse its full arc in both directions.

Replace the automatic bridge and oil top pivots of rotor and rocking arm.

Fig. 52 shows the oiling chart. Check that during the complete travel of the rotor three teeth of the fine-tooth ratchet are gathered up by the click on the top plate.

Apply the tests as noted on page 5.

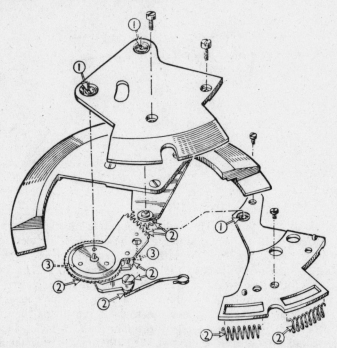

Fig. 52.—*Oiling chart for the Omega automatic. Arrow 1—Watch oil (thin oil). Arrow 2—Clock oil (thick oil). Dotted arrow 3—Smear with watch oil underneath part.*

PATEK PHILIPPE

The automatic watch made by Patek Philippe of Geneva, Switzerland, is known as Calibre 12′′′ 500. The quality of the movement is superb, the steelwork is straight-grained with edges broken and polished. The rotor revolves the full 360° and winds in both directions. In order that the rotor shall be of the *correct* weight a solid piece of 18 ct. gold is used. The action is very simple and most ingenious and there appears to be nothing to go wrong, its action is as follows (Fig. 53) :—

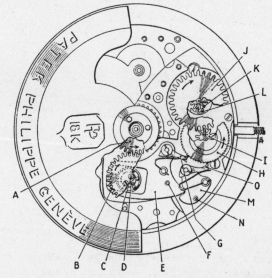

Fig. 53.—*The Patek Philippe automatic watch, which has a rotor of 18 ct. gold.*

For convenience of description the rotor is travelling anti-clockwise. Fixed to the rotor is the wheel *A* which gears with the wheel *B*. This wheel is pivoted at *C*. Secured to the wheel *B* is the ball-race *D* and it will be noted that it is screwed on out of centre so that as the wheel *B* rotates the race is eccentric. The cam *E*, pivoted at *F*, has a fork-like part which embraces the ball-race. The click *G*, with its spring, is pivoted on to the cam and engages with the ratchet wheel *H*. Fixed to the ratchet is the pinion *I* which gears with the wheel *J*, and fixed to this wheel is the pinion *K* which in turn gears with the transmission wheel *L*, and so to the main ratchet wheel squared on to the barrel arbor.

As the wheel *A* rotates in the direction of the arrow the wheel *B* will cause the ball-race to move the lever *E* upwards. This action will cause the click *G* to move the ratchet wheel *H* in the direction of the arrow and so eventually to wind the mainspring. When the rotor travels in a clockwise direction the cam *E* will be moved down and the click *G* will pass freely over the teeth of the ratchet wheel, but the end of the cam *E* engages the cam *M*, pivoted at *N*, and the click *O* with its spring, is pivoted on this cam. The movement causes the cam *M* to move up and thus the ratchet wheel *H* is impelled forward, again in the direction of the arrow.

Patek Philippe recommend the following procedure when dismantling the movement.

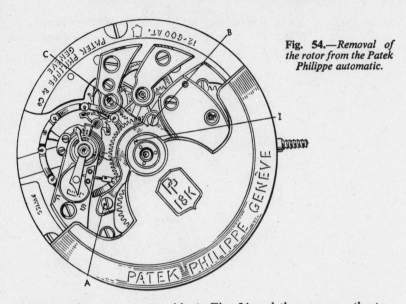

Fig. 54.—*Removal of the rotor from the Patek Philippe automatic.*

1. Move the rotor to one side as Fig. 54 and then remove the two screws *A* and *B*. Withdraw the steel locking piece *C* and this will release the rotor which can now be lifted up and away from the movement.

2. Remove the case ring.

3. Remove the bridge *A* Fig. 55, and the two wheels *B* and *C*.

4. Release the tension of the mainspring by disengaging the click *D* Fig. 55.

5. Remove the bridge *E* Fig. 55 and the parts *F*, *G* and *H*.

6. The movement is then dismantled in the conventional manner.

Special Note.—To release the mainspring it is preferable to remove the wheel *C* Fig. 55 first. This will then engage the click *D* Fig. 55 and the mainspring is allowed to be let down by controlling the winding button.

Re-assembling. Before assembling the automatic mechanism make sure the crown wheel, ratchet wheel and the transmission are perfectly free. The face of the ratchet wheel must be oiled.

The automatic work is then assembled in the same manner as it was taken to pieces, but in the reverse sequence, starting with the wheel *H* Fig. 55.

The Rotor. *Special attention.*—Make sure that the mark *I* on the rotor and the mark *J* on the wheel with the eccentric disc face each other, so as to ensure the maximum winding potential. Also see that the rotor is perfectly free.

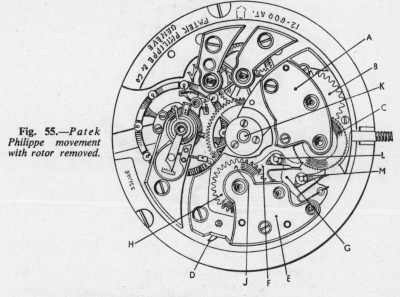

Fig. 55.—*Patek Philippe movement with rotor removed.*

Oiling.—Apply watch oil to all winding wheel pivots of the automatic winding mechanism : rotor arbor K ; click pivots L and M and very little on the teeth of the winding wheel C. Apply clock oil to the eccentric disc F; to the fork lever and to the point of the same lever where it engages the lever G.

Apply the test as noted on page 5.

PIERCE

The movement made by Pierce S.A., Bienne, Switzerland, is $8\frac{3}{4}'''$, CAL. 861 AUT., and is an exception inasmuch as it has no rotor. It is wound by a reciprocating weight which surrounds the movement. Fig. 56 is a general view of the movement. The action of the automatic mechanism is as follows : attached to the weight A (Fig. 57) is a rack with ratchet teeth B. This engages into a wheel with fine ratchet teeth C, and fixed to it is a pinion.

When this wheel is moved forward by the rack it is kept in position by the click and spring D. The pinion of this ratchet wheel engages into the wheel and pinion E. The pinion of the wheel E gears into the upper ratchet wheel F, which is squared on to the barrel arbor. The under ratchet wheel has a round hole and fits freely on the barrel arbor. This ratchet wheel is recessed to accommodate the two steel wheels as shown in Fig. 58. These two small wheels really constitute a form of ratchet work which is most ingenious. It operates as follows :—

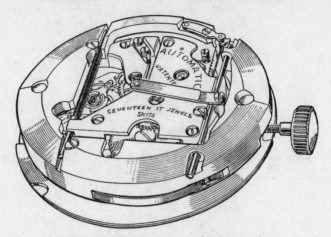

Fig. 56.—*Pierce automatic winding movement.*

When the autowinding is in action the lower ratchet remains stationary. The wheel 1 (Fig. 58) is squared on to the barrel arbor. The wheel 2 is fitted with one pivot only, which is located in the relatively large hole in the ratchet wheel. This enables the wheel to rock backward and forward ; therefore as the top ratchet wheel is made to rotate, the wheel 1 also rotates and with it the wheel 2 ; but if the power of the autowinding were taken off and the wheel 1 to reverse, a tooth of the wheel 2 will bank on the side of the recess as shown in Fig. 59. It will be seen, therefore, that if the lower ratchet wheel is made to rotate, as during manual winding, the wheel 2 (Fig. 59), butting on the recess, will cause the wheel 1 to rotate and so wind the mainspring ; in these circumstances, the click engaging the wheel moves and so holds up the mainspring. When autowinding, however, this click does not actually move but still holds up the mainspring.

The weight reciprocates at right-angles to the pendant, i.e. from 6 to 12. It is held in position and travels on the guide rods *G* and *H* (Fig. 57). The spiral spring, *F*, embracing the guide rod *H*, facilitates the return of the weight, ready to be jerked in the forward direction to wind.

To dismantle : first place the spring of the rack click *D* (Fig. 57) to the other side of the banking screw ; this will free the rack of the wheel it engages with. Remove the rack *B* by unscrewing the bridge, *J*, then withdraw the rack. Next let the power of the mainspring down in the conventional manner ; unscrew the three screws *K, L, M,* and the weight complete with the bridge, which forms the top plate of the automatic mechanism, can be lifted off and away from the movement. The wheel with ratchet teeth and the next wheel can now be removed. Unscrew the ratchet wheel screw and remove both the upper and lower wheels, together with the two small wheels.

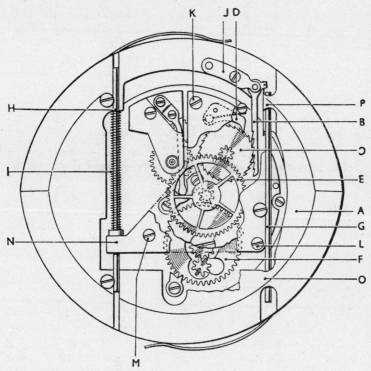

Fig. 57.—*The Pierce movement employs a reciprocating spring-loaded weight.*

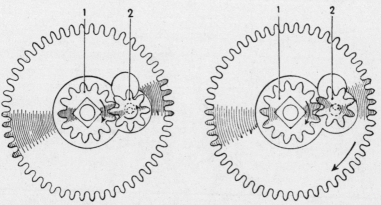

Fig. 58.—*The wheel 1 has only one pivot and can rock so that it can lock as in Fig. 59.*

Fig. 59.—*The wheel 2 has one tooth banked on the side of the recess.*

To re-assemble : after cleaning the movement and having fully assembled up to the automatic work, it is convenient to place the movement in its case to assemble the automatic mechanism. Oil with clock oil the pivot upon which the lower ratchet wheel fits, place the wheel on the barrel arbor square, then oil that part upon which the small wheel rests and place it in position. Now screw the top ratchet into position. Oil with watch oil the lower holes of the two autowind wheels and also the click, and place these parts into positon. Screw on the top plate with the weight. Insert the rack—apply a little watch oil to the teeth of the rack and grease with clock oil the guide rods where they contact the weight, i.e. at points *N, O, P* (Fig. 57)

To check after assembling : hold the watch vertically with the pendant on the left. Lift the weight up with a pointed peg and observe that the rack should gather up five teeth ; release the weight and it should drop to the bottom. Reverse the watch so that the pendant is at the right and, during the early stages of winding, the weight being lifted should wind as it falls. Eventually as the mainspring becomes wound the falling weight will not wind by virtue of its own weight alone, but will require a jerk. Oil with watch oil the pivot holes in the top plate. Finally, when winding manually, wind slowly, otherwise the rack teeth may be damaged.

REVUE

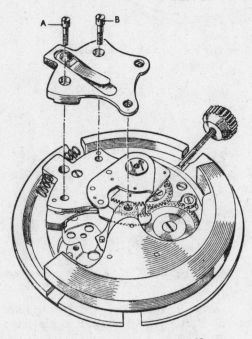

The Revue watch is made by Thommen Watch Co., Ltd., Waldenburg, Switzerland. The movement is $13\frac{1}{2}'''$, with $8\frac{3}{4}'''$ actual watch movement. Fig. 60 shows a general view ; the rotor operates through a segment of a circle with bumper springs, the mainspring being wound as the rotor rotates in either direction.

Fig. 60.—*Movement of the Revue automatic which winds in both di ections.*

The action of the automatic winding mechanism is as follows : fixed to the rotor is a steel pinion which gears into two sector rack gears. Fixed to each of the racks is a click and spring which operates upon a very fine ratchet toothed wheel ; this ratchet wheel has a pinion fixed to it. Therefore, as the rotor swings, one of the clicks gathers up the wheel and the other click is just made to free-wheel back ; reverse the direction of the rotor and the first-mentioned click will pass the teeth and the other click gathers up the wheel, always in the same forward direction. The pinion of the fine-toothed ratchet wheel gears into the transmission wheel of the keyless work. This system is simple and of sound design.

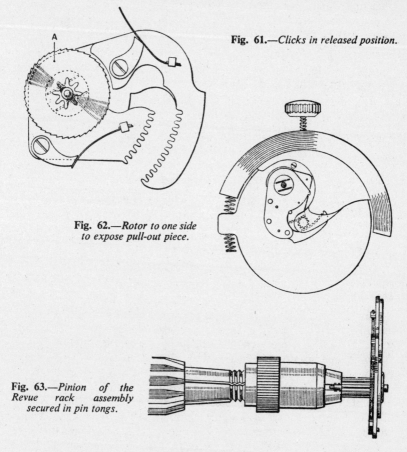

Fig. 61.—*Clicks in released position.*

Fig. 62.—*Rotor to one side to expose pull-out piece.*

Fig. 63.—*Pinion of the Revue rack assembly secured in pin tongs.*

To dismantle : the autowinding mechanism is removed before taking the movement from its case. Unscrew the top plate of the automatic work, A, B (Fig. 60), then cause the ratchet wheel A (Fig. 61) to move slightly by turning the winding button a little so as to release the tension of the mainspring on this wheel. Lift off the rotor and the sector rack assembly complete. The movement can now be removed from its case in the normal manner. If it is desired to remove the movement complete with the autowinding, move the rotor to one side, as in Fig. 62, to expose the pull-out piece screw. It is of vital importance that the automatic winding ratchet wheel shall not be injured, as the teeth are very fine and the wheel being made of brass is soft and easily damaged.

The rack assembly works without any oil or grease ; it operates efficiently when left quite dry. It is therefore not necessary to take it to pieces for purposes of cleaning, but should it be necessary to fit a new part to this assembly, proceed as follows to dismantle :—

First, arrange the two clicks as Fig. 61, then secure the arbor of the pinion in the pin tongs as Fig. 63 and with a screwdriver unscrew the screw as shown in Fig. 64.

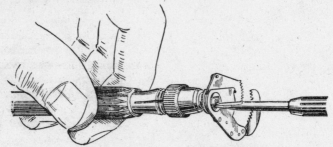

Fig. 64.—*Screwing up the rack assembly.*

After cleaning, assemble the movement in the normal manner. It is convenient to fit the movement into its case before assembling the automatic mechanism.

Having cleaned the parts of the automatic work, proceed to assemble as follows : if the sector rack has been dismantled, place the nut on a steel plate with a hole to receive the pivot of the ratchet wheel pinion. Arrange the clicks on the sectors as Fig. 61, place the larger sector in position on the nut, click upwards, then place the smaller sector in position, also with click upwards. Apply a little pressure with a piece of peg-wood to bind the steel nut. Now screw the ratchet wheel, held in the pin tongs, and screw up tightly (Fig. 65). The ratchet wheel should in the circumstances be held, since it would tend to loosen the pinion in the wheel and it is essential that this pinion should be fixed tightly. Release the clicks and see that they engage with the ratchet wheel correctly. Finally, ensure that the nut is tight.

Fig. 65.—*Method of holding rack assembly while re-assembling.*

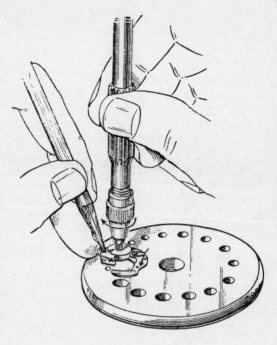

To reiterate : *it is important not to apply any oil or grease to this assembly.*

To continue with the general assembly of the automatic work: fit into position the sector assembly, first applying watch oil to the lower hole. Arrange the sectors so that the small hole in the base plate is in line with the rivet end of the click spring of the small sector. Apply clock oil to the lower hole of the rotor, then place the rotor in position so that it is midway between the bumper spring, as shown in Fig. 69. This will ensure the full and equal operation of the sector rack gears with the pinion of the rotor. It only remains to oil the two top pivots, the ratchet wheel and the rotor, and the work is complete.

Test the rotor as explained on page 5.

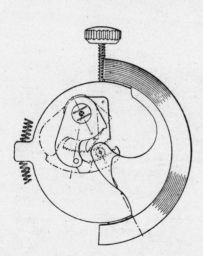

Fig. 66.—*Seeing that the Revue rack segments are in alignment.*

ROLEX

There are two models of the Rolex automatic winding watch, made by the Rolex Watch Co. of Geneva, Switzerland: the Tudor Prince Cal. 390 and the Rolex Perpetual Cal. 1000. As the fundamental principle of the automatic mechanism is similar in both watches, the Cal. 1000 will be described since this is the best known Rolex model at the time of writing.

Where the Cal. 1000 differs from the Tudor in part is that the Cal. 1000 is more highly finished. It is fitted with 21 jewels and an improved shock-absorbing system to the balance staff; the top escape wheel jewel hole, and end-stone are detachable. This system facilitates the adjustment of the endshake of the escape wheel and is convenient for the removal of these jewels should partial cleaning be necessary.

The Tudor has 17 jewels.

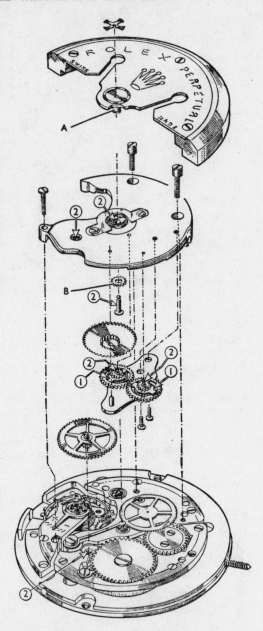

Fig. 67.—*Exploded view and oiling chart of the Rolex Cal. 1000 automatic. Arrow 1. Watch oil (thin oil). Arrow 2.—Clock oil (thick oil).*

In both calibres the rotor revolves the full 360 degrees, winding in both directions.

The action is as follows : the rotor arbor *A* (Fig. 67), which is riveted to the rotor, has two flats cut on its lower end. These fit into a similarly shaped hole in a small steel wheel *B* which gears into one of two brass (nickelled) wheels. These two wheels—the reverser wheels—*C* (Fig. 68) are exactly similar. They are each fitted with a fixed ratchet wheel *D* (Fig. 69) and two long loose clicks *E*. The two clicks are held in position by a ring *F* which is snapped on in similar fashion to a barrel cover. Over this ratchet wheel and clicks is fitted a pinion *G* fixed to a type of lock-washer plate *H*.

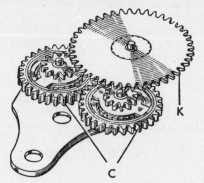

Fig. 68.—*The reverser wheels.*

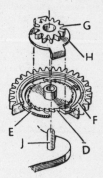

Fig. 69.—*Parts of a re-verser wheel.*

The wheels and the pinions are free to rotate on studs *J* which are riveted to the plate carrying the wheels. Both the pinions gear into a brass wheel with pinion *K* (Fig. 70) which also fits on a stud riveted to the plate. Therefore, if one of the reverser wheels *C* is made to rotate in either direction, the wheel *K* will rotate in one direction by virtue of the heads of the clicks pressing upon the rectangular plates to which the pinions are fixed ; one pair of clicks will idle over its ratchet wheel while the other pair is being pulled round the heads pushing the pinion through the rectangular plate. When the direction of rotation is reversed the second pair of clicks comes into action. The pinion of *K* gears into another brass wheel with pinion *L* (Fig. 71) and it is the pinion of this last wheel which gears direct into the ratchet wheel of the barrel.

Although the system may sound complicated to describe it is, in fact, simple and, what is more important, quite obvious and straight-forward, presenting no difficulty to the skilled watch repairer.

To dismantle, first let down the mainspring in the conventional manner, then remove the movement from its case. Unscrew the three screws *W*, *X*, *Y* (Fig. 70) and lift up and away from the movement the automatic bridge complete with the rotor. The movement will then be left with the wheel *L* (Fig. 71) gearing into the barrel ratchet wheel. Remove this wheel. Now place the automatic unit on a stake as in Fig. 73 and remove the rotor locking disc *M* (Fig. 70) with the blade of a screwdriver, pressing against the edge with the slot, as shown. This will release the rotor post and with it the small steel wheel *B* (Fig. 67) with the rounded end and a rectangular hole. Lift the rotor up and away from the unit.

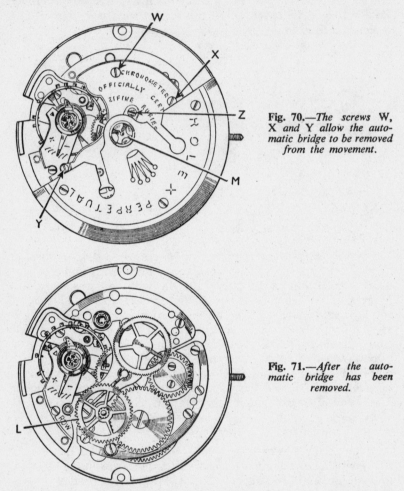

Fig. 70.—*The screws* W, X *and* Y *allow the automatic bridge to be removed from the movement.*

Fig. 71.—*After the automatic bridge has been removed.*

Next place the automatic bridge upside-down on the bench and remove the two screws *U* and *V* (Fig. 72) and prise up the plate.

The three wheels under this plate are almost sure to come away with the plate. Then remove the brass wheel K and the two reverser wheels C from their studs (Fig. 68). The pinions are lifted out of the wheels and the clicks E (Fig. 71) are removed by prising up the steel snap-on ring F (Fig. 69). To do this without injury use a piece of brass wire filed up like a screwdriver blade.

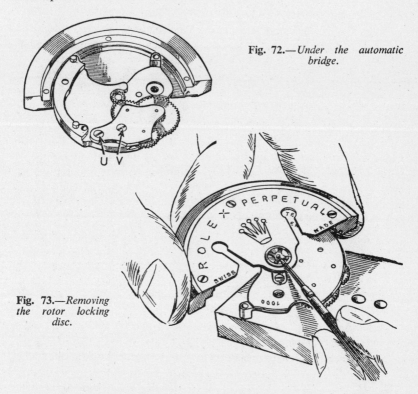

Fig. 72.—*Under the automatic bridge.*

Fig. 73.—*Removing the rotor locking disc.*

Should it be required to fit a new mainspring only it is not necessary to take the automatic mechanism to pieces. Remove screw Z (Fig. 70) and then turn the rotor to expose the other screw. Unscrew this screw half a turn and spring the steel plate round to one side. This will release the large jewel hole and it will be possible to remove the whole of the automatic mechanism as one unit.

Re-Assembly

Having cleaned the movement and all the automatic components in the usual manner and reassembled the movement, the automatic work may be assembled.

55

Place the plate with the studs upside-down on the bench (Fig. 68). Apply a little watch oil to each of the three studs then place the two reverser wheels *C* in position. Fit in the clicks *E* and snap the ring *F* into position. See that the clicks are equidistant so that when the pinions *G* (Fig. 69) are placed in position the projections of the lock washer type plates *H* to which the pinions are fixed fit between the head of one click and the tail of the other.

Apply a fair amount of watch oil to the teeth of the ratchet wheels *D*. Place the brass wheel *K* in position. With the automatic bridge flat on the bench place the plate with its three wheels in position and screw down, the wheels will not drop off as the oil holds them in position.

Move one of the steel wheels *C* backward and forward to ensure they are free and that the reverser action is correct. The brass wheel *K* should move in one direction only.

Now place the rotor upside-down on the bench and oil the rotor post with clock oil. Next place the automatic bridge on to the rotor, also upside-down. Fit the small steel wheel *B* into the end of the rotor arbor, recessed side uppermost, and place the rotor fixing post into the centre of the rotor arbor.

Hold the assembly in the left hand—in tissue paper—with the fore-finger of the left hand pressing against the end of the rotor fixing post. and in this position turn the assembly over and replace the locking disc. It will be found that with slight pressure, using the blade of a screwdriver, it snaps into position once the slotted side has been presented to the groove in the end of the fixing post.

Apply clock oil to the lower hole of the wheel *L* which gears into the barrel ratchet wheel and place that wheel in position. Now fit the automatic unit on to the movement. See that the pinion of the brass wheel *K* between the plates engages into the brass wheel *L* (Fig. 71). Manipulate the top pivot of wheel *L* into its hole and screw the bridge down. Apply a little clock oil to the top pivot of wheel *L* and the assembly is complete. See oiling chart (Fig. 67). Apply the tests as noted on page 5.

Two improvements in connection with the case are worth mention-ing. Rolex have reverted to the screw-down type of button we are familiar with in their Oyster watches. It is now vastly improved inasmuch as that even if the button is not screwed down at all it is still waterproof ; thus it is a double waterproof system.

The glass fits on to an outside rim of the case. It is then made doubly secure by a ring pressed over the glass and gripping the side of the glass. The advantages of this system are that it provides a double lock and a new glass can be fitted without removing the movement from its case or even opening it. The ring is removed with the blade of a knife as one would open an ordinary bezel.

The general construction and finish of this movement is of a high order and the reverser system is most ingenious and certainly unique.

ROTOMATIC (Ebauches, S.A.)

Made by A. Schild S.A., Grenchen, Switzerland, the Rotomatic has an $11\frac{1}{2}'''$ movement = 26 mm. calibre No. 1361. The rotor rotates through 360° and winds in both directions, and there is a centre seconds hand. The movement is shown in Fig. 19 and, with the dial removed in Fig. 20.

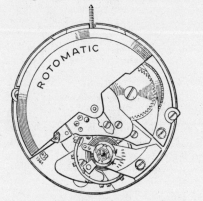

Fig. 74.—*Rotomatic movement showing 360° rotor.*　　**Fig. 75.**—*Movement with dial removed.*

To remove the movement from its case, turn the dog screws A and B (Fig. 76). Remove the winding shaft and the movement can be lifted from the case. To take the automatic mechanism to pieces remove the click bridge A (Fig. 78) and the click. Refit the winding shaft and then let the mainspring down by holding back the ratchet click, controlling it by the winding button. Then remove the three screws C, D, and E (Fig. 76). The top plate of the automatic work can now be lifted off and with it the rotor.

The action is as follows : a brass wheel B (Fig. 77) fixed to the rotor gears into first one steel wheel and then the other, C, which are both pivoted upon a small steel rocking arm D. The arm rocks to and fro and as the rotor wheel engages forward with one wheel when rotating in one direction, and then as the rotor rotates in the reverse direction it disengages and engages forward with the other wheel, with the result that the wheel and rocking bar wheels engage into E alternately, causing it to rotate in one direction only. A click engages

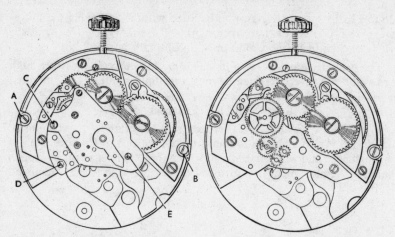

Fig. 76.—*Rotomatic movement with rotor removed.*   **Fig. 77.**—*Rotomatic showing automatic mechanism with plate removed.*

the last-mentioned wheel and this wheel engages another wheel with pinion attached, *F*. This pinion in turn engages a steel wheel *G* with a loose pinion *H*, the lower end of which is cut with ratchet teeth engaging another ratchet fixed to the wheel similar in action to the crown and castle wheels of keyless work. The result is that the pinion can rotate in one direction only. This ratchet pinion gears into the transmission wheel *I* and so to the main ratchet of the movement and thus the mainspring is wound.

As the rotor moves in either direction the wheel next to the rocking arm is held up by the click until the click of the ratchet wheel takes over, thus the greatest advantage is taken of every movement of the rotor.

When winding up the mainspring by the winding button, the ratchet pinion of the last wheel of the automatic train just reverses, so that the wheels of the automatic work are not made to rotate. The ratchet pinion is kept in contact with the ratchet in the wheel by a spring *J* (Fig. 78). Fig. 77 shows the train of the automatic work. The movement is so designed that the barrel can be removed, to fit a new mainspring, without even taking the movement from its case. To continue taking to pieces the rotor is removed by unscrewing the steel plate *K* (Fig. 78) on the top plate of the automatic work. The up-and-down movement of the rotor is controlled by the spring *K* (Fig. 78). To give less freedom the knib of this spring should be bent upwards and to give more freedom it should be bent down. For method of oiling refer to Fig. 78. Finally, apply the test for freedom of rotor as explained in page 5.

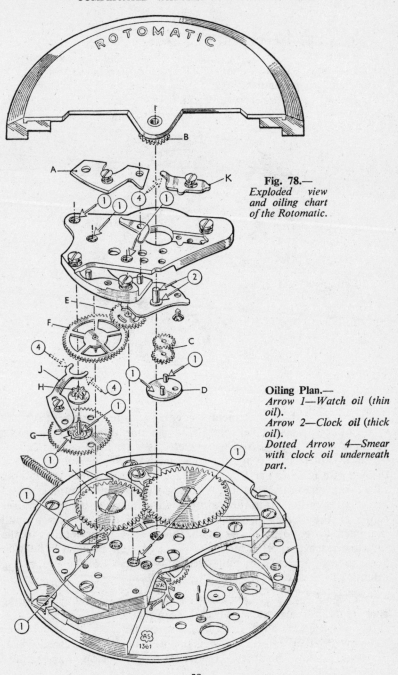

Fig. 78.—
Exploded view and oiling chart of the Rotomatic.

Oiling Plan.—
Arrow 1—Watch oil (thin oil).
Arrow 2—Clock oil (thick oil).
Dotted Arrow 4—Smear with clock oil underneath part.

59

TISSOT

Made by Chs. Tissot et Fils S.A., Le Locle, Switzerland, there are three Tissot models with centre seconds hands and three with off-set seconds hands, diameters being 28.00 mm., 28.50 mm. and 31.00 mm. The automatic mechanism is the same in each model. Calibres are 28-1 28.5-1, 31-1 off-set seconds and 28-21, 28.5-21, 31-21 centre seconds. *See* Fig. 79 for general view of the movement.

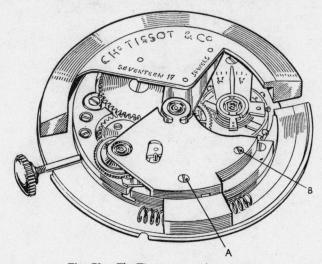

Fig. 79.—*The Tissot automatic movement.*

The rotor oscillates a segment of a circle and the movement is fitted with buffer springs. The rotor winds in one direction only. The action is as follows : Fixed to the rotor is a steel bar on the end of which are cut teeth *A* (Fig. 80), these teeth gearing into a rack cut on the end of a rocking bar *B*. Attached to this rocking bar is a ratchet wheel with pinion fixed to it. A click *C* engages in the ratchet wheel and the pinion gears into the transmission wheel. As the rotor moves to the left the rocking arm moves to the right and gathers up in a full movement three teeth of the ratchet, when the rotor returns to the right the ratchet wheel is moved forward to the right, and is held up in position by the click *D*, until eventually the click of the mainspring ratchet wheel takes over.

To dismantle, first release the click *D* (Fig. 80) so that the mainspring click holds the main ratchet wheel. Then remove the two screws *A, B* (Fig. 78). Lift the top plate of the automatic work off. The rotor can now be lifted free of the movement. Remove the rocking bar. To clean, remove the three screws holding the rocking bar ratchet ;

60

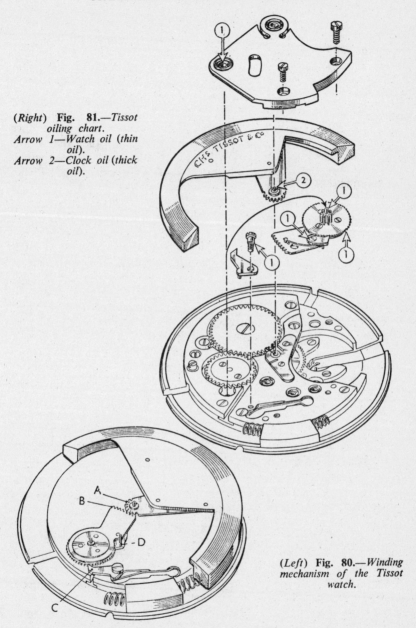

(*Right*) **Fig. 81.**—*Tissot oiling chart.*
Arrow 1—Watch oil (thin oil).
Arrow 2—Clock oil (thick oil).

(*Left*) **Fig. 80.**—*Winding mechanism of the Tissot watch.*

it is essential that the bearing of this wheel shall be perfectly clean and free. When reassembling the rocking bar, oil the bearing of the ratchet

61

wheel with watch oil before screwing it into position. Place the rotor in position and hold the rotor against the right-hand buffer spring ; now place the rocking bar in position so that the last space of the rack teeth embraces the first tooth of the steel rack attached to the rotor. It is then certain that the rack of the rotor engages for the full segment of movement of the teeth of the rocking bar.

The rotor must not bank on the teeth of the rocking bar rack, but on the bumper springs. Fig. 80 shows the correct position. Place the click D in position, Fig. 80, with its spring, and then the bridge. Oil the pivots of the rotor with clock oil and the pivots of the rocking arm with watch oil. Apply a little watch oil to the teeth of the rocking arm ratchet wheel. Oil the shoulders of the two clicks controlling the rocking arm ratchet wheel with watch oil, sparingly. See Fig. 81, the oiling chart.

The instructions given by Messrs. Tissot when re-assembling are as follows : The automatic winding mechanism of a Tissot watch is remarkably simple yet in order to secure perfect running, its assembling requires the greatest accuracy. Therefore, we particularly insist on the importance of the following directions to ascertain that all parts are correctly located.

(1) Move the rotor to and fro on the buffer springs, to make sure that the racks are properly meshed. The rotor should not stop before reaching either buffer spring. If it stops before the end of the swing, the respective position of the racks must be altered. They should gear as shown in Fig. 80.

(2) Check the position of the rotor : it should touch neither plate nor case.

(3) Control the end-shake of the rotor and of the small ratchet. The end-shake should not exceed 2/100 of a millimetre.

(4) Make sure that both racks are positioned on the same level.

(5) Examine the retaining click work. The small ratchet is to move by three teeth forward at each useful oscillation of the rotor.

(6) Check the end-shake of the retaining click.

Finally apply the tests as given on page 5.

ULTRA

In the Ultra automatic made by Ultra, Besançon, Doubs, France, Fig. 82, the rotor revolves the full 360° and winds in both directions. The action is as follows : the rotor is squared on to a short arbor which is pivoted in jewelled bearings. Fixed to the arbor on which the rotor is squared and held in position by the screw A, Figs. 82 and 83, is an eccentric cam B and fitted to a chariot C are two jewel rollers

D free to rotate. These rollers straddle the cam and as the rotor oscillates it causes the chariot to rock backward and forward. Fig. 83 shows the inside of the automatic frame ; the rotor is screwed to the outside.

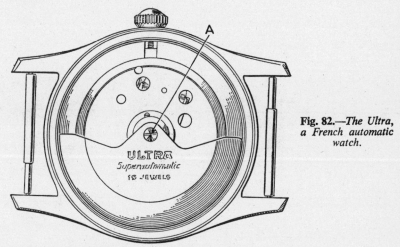

Fig. 82.—*The Ultra, a French automatic watch.*

Fixed at one end of the chariot are two long clicks with springs combined, *E*, (Fig. 83), the ends engaging the teeth of a fine ratchet-toothed wheel *F*, which has fixed to it a pinion *G*. As the chariot is made to move upwards, the left-hand click pushes the wheel *F* forward, and as the chariot moves downward, the right-hand click pulls the wheel down, therefore the wheel *F* always rotates in the same direction as arrow.

Shoulder screw *A* holds one end of the chariot down and the wheel *F* the other ; the wheel is screwed to the frame by a shouldered screw.

The whole of the automatic mechanism is fitted to the underside of a cap or frame which fits over the watch movement. Two dumb-bell shaped springs *H* keep the chariot central so that the fullest advantage is taken of the slightest movement of the rotor. The pinion *G* gears direct into the main ratchet wheel of the watch movement.

The ratchet wheel Fig. 84, consists of four parts. The wheel itself has a very large round hole and into a recess cut into its under surface fits a steel disc with a square hole. A round domed spring washer fits into the large hole of the ratchet wheel and a flat washer fits into a recess cut into the upper surface. When this washer is screwed home it compresses the spring washer to form a slipping device. A slipping mainspring is not employed.

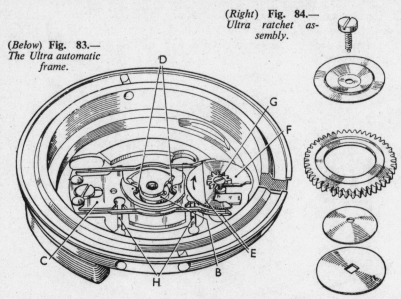

(*Right*) **Fig. 84.—** *Ultra ratchet assembly.*

(*Below*) **Fig. 83.—** *The Ultra automatic frame.*

To dismantle : Remove the winding shaft by unscrewing the pull-out piece screw through the hole in the automatic frame. The movement will then drop out of its case. Unscrew the screw set into the side of the frame one turn. Press gently against the anti-dust sleeve of the movement with a piece of peg-wood to start separating the frame from the movement. Complete the removal of the movement by placing the blade of a screw-driver under each of the two lips on the movement and levering it gently against the edge of the frame.

To dismantle the automatic unit, first unscrew the rotor screw *A*, Fig. 82, and remove the rotor. Then remove the screw holding the fine-toothed ratchet wheel and also the screw at the other end of the chariot. Lever up the two dumb-bell shaped springs very carefully, making sure the chariot is in its correct position before lifting off, i.e. that the two jewel rollers are free of the lower potance of the rotor arbor. Push this plate out from the underside with a piece of peg-wood. Ultra advise that the parts of the automatic work be cleaned in benzine with a small brush. The frame and the rotor are cleaned in the usual manner. They also advise that when it is necessary to replace certain parts sub-units should be used.

Fig. 85 shows the sub-units ; it will be seen by the grouping that if, for instance, one of the jewel rollers is damaged, the complete unit will be replaced.

To re-assemble, first replace the rotor staff and the top jewel setting with the three small screws. See that the staff has little end-shake.

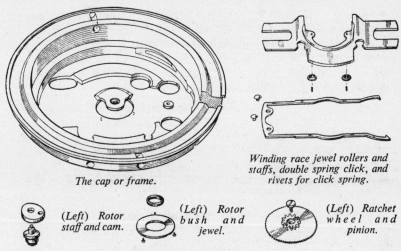

The cap or frame.

Winding race jewel rollers and staffs, double spring click, and rivets for click spring.

(Left) Rotor staff and cam.

(Left) Rotor bush and jewel.

(Left) Ratchet wheel and pinion.

Fig. 85.—*Ultra sub-units.*

Hold the top pivot by the square and see that the frame rotates flat. Next ensure that the two jewel rollers are quite free to rotate.

Fit the chariot into position and screw the fine-toothed ratchet wheel in and also the shouldered screw at the other end of the chariot. See that the spring clicks bear correctly on the wheel.

When replacing the rotor on the square of its arbor, position it so that the centre of the rotor points midway between the figures 1 and 2 o'clock on the dial of the watch, when the chariot is in its quiescent position. In other words, note some point on the automatic frame the position of 1 and 2 o'clock when the frame is fitted on the movement and then place the rotor on the square so that the centre of the weight points to that mark.

Oiling

Ultra recommend that both the pivots of rotor arbor and the shoulder of the fine-toothed ratchet wheel should be oiled with Chronax D, the shoulder of fine-toothed ratchet wheel screw with Chronax H, and the parts in contact in the main ratchet wheel assembly with activated grease. *See* page 4.

To adjust the tension spring of the main ratchet wheel proceed as follows : Before fitting the automatic mechanism in position wind by the winding button.

When the mainspring is fully unwound hold the ratchet wheel with a piece of peg-wood and tighten the screw so that the upper washer fits squarely on the ratchet wheel. Now wind the watch and count the number of turns of the ratchet wheel screw until the clutch begins to slip. Tighten up the ratchet wheel screw further, if necessary, so that slipping does not take place until after 5½ to 6½ turns of the screw ; this will ensure the watch going for from 36 to 41 hours. When the movement and the automatic unit have been overhauled and assembled, the re-assembling of the two units is simple.

Next place the movement in the frame and turn the winding shaft slightly to engage the pinion of the five-toothed ratchet wheel with the teeth of the main ratchet wheel. Press the movement home firmly and make secure by tightening the screw in the side of the frame. Owing to its construction it is not possible to apply the usual test as noted in page 5, but it is sufficient to see that the rotor rotates freely as the movement is turned.

A comprehensive selection of automatic winding watches has now been described and their servicing detailed. Those dealt with do not, and could not, include all the systems in use at the present time, but the fundamentals have been covered. New models are constantly being put on to the market and almost weekly a new one appears.

I am convinced that we have not yet reached the " final " Automatic model, either as regards simplicity of design or perfection of principle : there is so much to commend automatic winding and it may well be that some years will pass before a more or less basic system is evolved. One can almost compare the keyless watch and the key wind, with the automatic winding and present-day keyless mechanism. It would seem that as soon as a " perfect " system is evolved something entirely revolutionary makes its appearance.

Section 2

THE CHRONOGRAPH

This heading " Chronograph," covers a vast number of applications, but the fundamentals are very similar. The chronograph is, as its name implies, a recorder of time and it is usual to apply the word chronograph to a watch or instrument, it may be a clock, which tells the time of day and also has fitted to it a mechanism which can be put into operation at will to record an interval of time. A watch that records an interval of time only is called a timer. The mechanism which is put into operation to record an interval of time, whether it is fitted to a chronograph proper or a timer, is similar in each case. We shall, however, deal with the chronograph first.

Up to recent years, the operation of the chronograph was from one push, usually at the winding button.   One push to start the chronograph hand running, second push to stop, and the third push to return to zero.   The modern chronograph—largely in the form of a wrist-watch—is fitted with two push pieces.   One of the push pieces is to

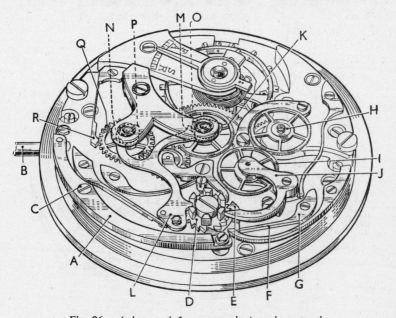

Fig. 86.—*A three push from one push piece chronograph.*

start and stop the chronograph mechanism and the other push piece to return to zero., there is a variation of this, one push to start and the other to stop and return to zero.

The illustration Fig. 86 is of the three push from one push piece type, and to describe the action of this, gives the fundamental principle of all chronographs. The lever *A* is pushed in at *B* by the action of push pins at the end of the winding button—or the button itself sliding on the winding shaft—this contacts a steel tube which impinges upon a stud riveted to the lever *A*. As this lever pivots at the shouldered screw *C*, it pulls round the column wheel *D* by means of the pawl *E*. When the tooth of the column wheel has been gathered up, the lever *A* returns to its normal position under the tension of the spring *F*, and the column wheel is held in position by the jumper spring *G*. The wheel *H* is fitted friction tight on to the extended pivot of the fourth wheel and is in constant gear with the wheel *I*, which is pivoted on to and carried by the lever *J*. As the nose of the lever *J* drops between the castellated column wheel it allows the wheel *I* to gear into the chronograph wheel *K* and so the chronograph wheel hand, which is fitted to the pivot of the wheel *K*, starts to rotate.

As the castle wheel rotates one ratchet tooth, the lever *J* will drop between the castellations or columns as indicated by the arrow in Fig. 87, and the wheel *I* will be in gear with the wheel *K*. A second push on to the winding button will cause the column wheel to rotate and lift up the lever *J* indicated by the arrow in Fig. 88, and so disconnect the wheel *I* from the wheel *K*, and the chronograph hand will stop. Thus a reading of the duration of the run can be observed by the position of the hand pointing to the scale on the dial.

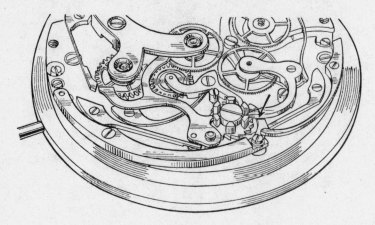

Fig. 87.—*The chronograph mechanism engaged.*

A third push of the button will cause the column to rotate and the lever J will stay on the block of the column wheel and the lever L will drop between the blocks, and in so doing, the ends M and N will contact the heart pieces O and P, and return these two wheels to the zero position. Heart pieces are fixed to both the chronograph wheel and the minute counter.

Minute Counter

The wheel Q is the minute counter and has fitted to its extended pivot the minute counter hand. This wheel is held in position during operation by a jumper spring, R (Fig. 86). A fingerpiece A (Fig. 88) is fixed to the chronograph wheel and as it revolves it contacts the wheel B (Fig. 88) and moves in on one tooth. This wheel gears into the minute counter wheel and it moves that wheel one tooth, so that for each revolution of the chronograph wheel the minute counter wheel is moved one tooth and the hand fixed to it points the number of revolutions of the chronograph wheel. In other words, it counts the minutes.

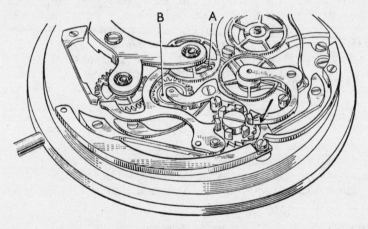

Fig. 88.—*The fingerpiece is shown at* A.

Some chronographs are fitted with another lever, as in Fig. 89. This is the brake. When the chronograph mechanism is at the stop position, the lever drops between the column blocks and the curved end with a radius exactly similar to that of the chronograph wheel, touches the periphery and so holds that wheel firm. The advantage is that if there is an interval between the stopping of the chronograph and the reading, there is no fear of the wheel moving, owing to vibration, etc. causing an incorrect registration to be made. When the chronograph mechanism is at zero and start, the brake is held on the top of the column blocks and so clear of the chronograph wheel ; it only comes into action at the stop action.

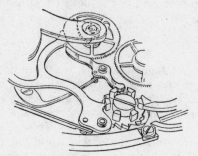

Fig. 89.—*The brake.*

Studying the Action

Before dismantling the movement, even before removing it from its case, carefully study the action of the mechanism. The beginner should spend at least five minutes observing what takes place when the chronograph is set in motion. Five minutes may not sound a long time, but just to watch and study, it is a good time and time well spent. Before even starting to take the movement to pieces, the student should be fully conversant with each part and know what takes place when the different parts are brought into action. The competent craftsman is able to reassemble the movement should it be handed to him completely dismantled and the parts shaken up to ensure thorough mixing. He would be able to assemble with ease because he *knows* how the watch works. With all complicated work, from the simple chronograph to the triple complicated movement, you must first know what you are doing. This is the secret of success with all complicated work.

Having thoroughly acquainted yourself with the *action* of the mechanism, proceed to dismantle it. When a part is removed, say a spring, associate its screw with it. Screws may be of different lengths, even if the heads are of the same size, and to keep them in order is to save time eventually and may well prevent damage. It is not practicable to give a sequence order for dismantling ; there are so many types of chronograph, that no good purpose would be served. One or two broad hints may, however, be given. For instance, most springs working on levers, etc., are in tension, therefore unscrew a little so to enable the spring to be lifted out of action and relieve the tension before finally unscrewing, otherwise there is the

70

risk of the spring flying when it is unscrewed. See that the top parts are removed first, do not blindly unscrew all screws, but dismantle systematically.

Special care should be taken not to touch the heads of the eccentric studs ; they have heads with slits just like screws for which they may easily be mistaken. To touch these studs means re-adjustment. *See* Fig. 110 where eccentric studs are numbered 1 to 4.

Cleaning

Having dismantled the movement, clean all the parts in the conventional manner (*see* " Practical Watch Repairing "). Well peg out the holes in the levers and see that the studs into which they fit are perfectly clean and free from congealed oil. The teeth of the fine-toothed chronograph wheels are cleaned with a glass brush, in addition to the usual cleaning with the machine or with benzine. These brushes can be purchased from the tool dealer and consist of a bundle of fine threads of glass bound together with string. Hold the wheel in tissue paper, between the thumb and first finger of the left hand, and with the end of the glass brush, brush the teeth as shown in Fig. 90. Continue to brush until the metal between the teeth glistens, then move the wheel round a little and brush again. Continue thus until all the teeth of the wheel are perfectly clean and bright.

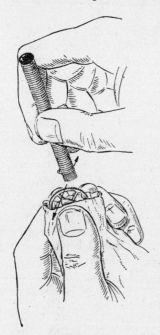

As the brush wears down, the string is untied to release a further portion of the threads ; it is advisable to use the brush with the glass short so that it is stiff and cuts well.

This treatment refers particularly to the very fine toothed wheels, usually the centre chronograph wheel, and in some watches all the chronograph wheels.

Assembling complicated Watches

While cleaning the movement pay particular attention to the centre wheel of the going train. Fitted into the hollow centre pinion is a bush with a hole drilled into it to receive the lower pivot of the centre chronograph wheel. After this wheel has been through the cleaning machine,

Fig. 90.—*Cleaning the teeth with a glass brush.*

sharpen a piece of watch peg-wood to a long, thin and almost parallel point. Peg the hole from the end opposite to where the common pinion fits, using light pressure to avoid disturbing the bush. After the first application, scrape the peg clean and apply again, continuing thus until the peg leaves the hole clean. Then repeat the operation from the short end. When you are satisfied that the hole is perfectly clean, hold the nose of the bellows up close to the hole of the pinion (Fig. 91) and give several hard puffs. Repeat this from both ends. It is essential that both the hole in the bush and the hollow of the centre shall be free from dust.

Fig. 91.—*Ensuring that there is no dust in the hole.*

If you have reason to believe that the hollow of the centre wheel is particularly dirty, it can be cleaned in the following manner. Stand the centre wheel upright on the end of its pinion, cannon pinion end up, in a bath of perfectly clean benzine, which is sufficiently deep to cover the uppermost end and leave it there for at least 30 minutes. It will be found that this procedure will remove all dirt and old oil from inside the hollow.

Having cleaned the whole of the movement and assembled the train up to, but not including the escapement, proceed to assemble the chronograph mechanism. Before replacing any of the chronograph parts, oil the pivot holes which will be covered by the parts.

First fit the column wheel into position, applying a little clock oil to the shoulder of the screw. Next screw the tension spring into position. There are two systems of spring ; one where the spring bears on the side of the arbor of the centre chronograph wheel, and the other where it bears on the under side of the minute counter finger piece or on to a boss fixed to the chronograph wheel. In the case of the former, see that the spring is positioned about halfway across the hole of the hollow centre pinion ; this will give it about the required tension when the arbor is in position. Where the spring bears on to a flat surface see that the spring will be free of the centre chronograph wheel arbor.

Screw the minute counter intermediate wheel into position, having first fitted the wheel on to the lever and oiled the shoulder screw with a little watch oil ; also oil, with clock oil, the shoulder screw of the lever. Next fit the spring which operates on the last-named lever and apply a little clock oil to the nose of this spring. Screw into position the column wheel jumper spring and also the stop-start lever with the pawl attached ; oil the shoulder screw of this lever with clock oil and also apply some to the ratchet teeth of the column wheel and to the pawl where it is pivoted on to the lever. As a general rule, it is better partly to screw down a spring and then to strain the spring carefully into position so that it works upon the part it is intended to before finally screwing down. If this procedure is adopted the risk of breaking the spring is minimised since the spring is not unduly strained ; the securing point of the spring gives as the screw is loose.

Next fix into position the intermediate minute counter wheel lever, having first screwed the wheel on to the lever, applying a little watch oil to the shoulder screw. Some chronographs are made with a cock T-screw to hold the intermediate wheel—the wheel is pivoted—in these circumstances apply a little watch oil to both pivots. Give the wheel a puff with the bellows, directing the air on to the sides of the teeth (Fig. 92) to ensure that it spins freely. Then apply a little clock

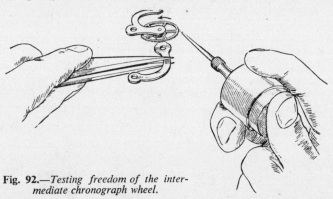

Fig. 92.—*Testing freedom of the intermediate chronograph wheel.*

oil to the shoulder of the lever screw and screw the lever into position. Fit the spring operating on this lever and apply a little clock oil to the nose where the spring impinges on the lever. Operate the column wheel to see that the last assembled lever operates correctly and also to work in the oil. It is good practice always to try each part as it is assembled rather than to make a complete assembly and then find something somewhere is not correct ; this principle applies equally to all assembly work. Next fit the chronograph wheel on to the extended fourth wheel and press carefully but firmly down ; remember you are pressing on to the lower jewel hole. Then assemble the intermediate chronograph wheel on to its lever and very lightly oil both pivots with watch oil. Give the wheel a puff with the bellows to ensure that it is perfectly free and spins easily. Oil with clock oil the side of the screw on to which this lever pivots. Now fit the spring operating on this lever and apply a little oil to the nose. Operate the stop-start lever to see that all is functioning well.

Observe that the wheel fitted on to the fourth wheel pivot gears correctly with the intermediate chronograph wheel on the same plane. If the wheel on the fourth pivot is too high it must be pressed down a little until it is the correct height. It should gear the full thickness of the wheel ; if, for instance, it engages only half the thickness of the wheel there is the danger, when the end-shakes are opposite, of the teeth becoming disengaged. On the other hand, if the wheel is low, then remove the wheel and close the hole in the wheel slightly. Invariably, there is an extended hole or boss and this can be gripped in a wire chuck—it should fit the hole in the chuck tightly—and the draw-in spindle made to rotate a little, so as to close the hole equally ; this is important because the wheel could be thrown out of upright and be made to run out of true in the round. Try the wheel on the pivot and if necessary to open the hole, broach from the underside with a round broach ; it is important not to remove any metal.

Hold the centre chronograph wheel as Fig. 93 and apply a minute quantity of watch oil to the shoulder of the lower pivot ; it needs only to be " greased." The Swiss generally advise that the pivots of the minute counter wheel and its intermediate wheel should not be oiled at all ; they argue that the action is light and practically frictionless and that oiling does more harm than good. Also with the same oiler, smear the underpart of the finger piece where the tension spring operates and then place the wheel carefully into position. Treat the pivot of the minute counter wheel in a similar manner and place that wheel in position. When placing the centre chronograph in position it is advisable to check the position of the tension

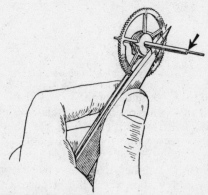

Fig. 93.—*Oiling the chronograph wheel pivot.*

74

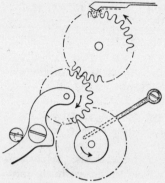

Fig. 94.—*Correct position of tension spring.*

spring and this applies to the type of spring which bears on a flat surface and not on the arbor. Visualise the direction of rotation of the wheel; the tension spring should be on the side of the arbor so that the wheel travels away from the spring and not towards it—disengaging and not engaging friction (Fig. 94). Some plates are so recessed that it is not possible to assemble the spring on the wrong side.

Now screw on the cock holding the top pivots of the two last-named wheels. Try the end-shakes of these wheels. If the tension is the type bearing on the flat surface of the finger piece or, as is sometimes the case, upon a boss, light downward pressure on the wheel is applied and it should return by virtue of the upward pressure of the spring. To complete the assembly fit on to its post the return to zero lever having first applied a little clock oil to the post. The spring of this lever not only acts as a spring but it also holds it down in position. Generally it is advisable to screw the spring into position first and then hold the nose of the spring to one side to allow the lever to drop down into position. See that this spring bears on the pin of the lever above the guide or boot. Apply a little clock oil to the nose of the spring.

I have advised oiling the pivots and the shoulders of shoulder screws of the chronograph wheels, i.e. the intermediate and centre chronograph wheels and the intermediate and minute counter wheels. To repeat, some craftsmen advise that these light-running wheels should not be oiled ; they reason that the oil drags and that there is little or no friction at these points. I cannot, however, bring myself to this point of view. I would rather say oil very lightly and with thin or light oil.

Testing Chronographs

The stage of assembly is now reached when the chronograph mechanism can be tested as a whole. First of all press the stop-start lever so that the mechanism is at stop, i.e. the intermediate wheel and the' return to zero lever are free of the centre chronograph wheel. With a fine pivot broach move the centre chronograph by an arm ; *never touch the teeth of any chronograph wheel with a metal tool :* they are so delicate and very easily damaged ; sometimes the damage can be so slight as to be hardly discernible, but disastrous to good running.

Lead the wheel round and see that the finger piece is quite free of the intermediate minute counter wheel and that the point of the heart cam is free of the head of the return to zero lever.

Now depress the start-stop lever to bring the return to zero lever into action and with the same pointer move the centre chronograph wheel so that the head of the return to zero travels up the sides of the heart piece. Move the wheel, say, a quarter of a turn and release ; the lever should return the wheel to the zero position smartly. Then move the wheel and try to make the head of the return to zero lever remain stationary on the point of the heart piece and then allow the wheel to return very slowly. For this part of the test to be correct it should not be possible for the heart piece fixed to the centre chronograph wheel to remain stationary in *any* position. There should be no dead point.

Should the return to zero lever stick, examine closely to discover why. There are two or three reasons ; one is, the shape of the heart cam itself. Generally, an incorrectly-formed heart cam is most unusual. The heart cam of the modern chronograph is carefully and mathematically plotted so that there are no " dead " points. The form of the curve on each side of the heart cam is the logarithmic curve or an Archimedean spiral and it is considered that the logarithmic curve is the more perfect. The heart piece cam is very hard and it is not likely that it can change shape unless it is wilfully altered. It is advisable, therefore, not to be tempted to touch the heart cam in order to alter its shape. If the edges of the cam show signs of damage, such as a bruise or burr, very carefully stroke the side with an Arkansas stone, only sufficient to remove the blemish, and then burnish well. Examine the head of the return to zero lever and see that it is free of blemishes ; here, again, if there are any marks, carefully stroke and burnish, making sure not to alter the original form or angle.

Should both the cam and the head of the lever appear to be correct the trouble may be in the angle of the head of the return to zero lever. To be correct the flat end of the head should be cut at an angle of 45 degrees from the line of centres (Fig. 95) or as near this angle as possible. The end of the head should be perfectly flat (from end to end, not the thickness of the lever) ; it should not be curved and neither should there be any rounding off of the ends. It should be just perfectly flat and sharp as in Fig. 96. Continuing the test, touch the chronograph wheel very lightly by an arm and see that the return to zero lever is holding it firmly. Now try the minute counter wheel and see if the lever is holding this firmly, too. If there is a slight movement of the minute wheel counter because the head is not quite hard against the apex of the heart, it is not material since the jumper spring will hold this wheel and in any case the reading of the hand on the dial is not critical. It is the centre chronograph wheel which must be firm so that there is no ambiguity about the zero position of the chronograph hand.

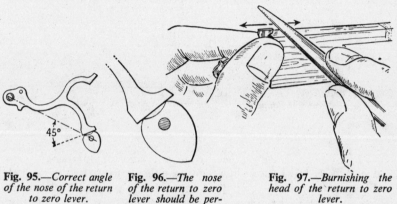

Fig. 95.—*Correct angle of the nose of the return to zero lever.*

Fig. 96.—*The nose of the return to zero lever should be perfectly flat.*

Fig. 97.—*Burnishing the head of the return to zero lever.*

If, on the other hand, the minute counter wheel is firm and there is the slightest movement of the centre chronograph wheel, then the head of the minute counter part of the return to zero lever must be reduced. To do this, stroke with an Arkansas slip, making sure to keep the angle as originally, then draw stroke with a 3—0 emery stick and finally burnish with an oval burnisher, using a draw file motion along the length of the head (Fig. 97). With the return to zero lever down on the heart pieces, see that the head of the jumper spring of the minute counter wheel is between two teeth. Otherwise, when the lever is lifted free of the heart piece the minute counter wheel will move by virtue of the jumper spring bringing the wheel into position. If it is found that the head of the jumper spring is lifted then the spring must be moved slightly so that the V of the head is safely between the teeth. Sometimes the jumper spring is adjustable and can be moved with ease, but if there is no form of adjustment the side of the head must be stoned so as to allow the V to drop in. Fig. 98 shows the fault and the dotted line the correction, but before altering the shape of the head, observe the minute counter action to be explained later.

Chronograph Wheel Depth

Next it is necessary to assemble the escapement before the chronograph examination can be completed. Wind up the mainspring and press the button to start the chronograph running. Examine with the double eyeglass the depth of the intermediate chronograph wheel with the centre wheel ; to be correct the depth should be as in Fig. 99. Some chronographs are made with the teeth of the centre chronograph wheel the same pitch as the intermediate wheel and others are made with double the number of teeth in the centre wheel (Fig. 100). It is

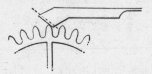

Fig. 98.—*Adjustment to nose of minute counter wheel jumper.*   Fig. 99.—*Correct chronograph wheel depth.*   Fig. 100.—*Correct depth with double the number of teeth in the centre chronograph wheel.*

more usual for the centre wheel to have double the number of teeth and it is better so because it is not so difficult to make intersection without movement of the centre wheel. If the pitch of both wheels is coarse there is the possibility of the intermediate wheel pushing the centre wheel backward or forward, *before* correct gearing takes place and therefore an accurate reading of the chronograph hand on the dial is not possible.

Observe very closely the *precise moment* when the intermediate wheel is released and gearing takes place ; if the teeth of the intermediate wheel do not immediately drop between the centre wheel teeth then the wheel fitted on to the pivot of the fourth wheel must be moved round slightly. To consider an extreme case, the points of the teeth may meet and it may be one or two-fifths of a second before the gears settle down ; or it may be a fifth of a second because the teeth intersect on the sides of the teeth ; they should drop in fully to be correct and this can be attained by adjusting the wheel on the fourth wheel.

Some chronograph adjusters start by setting the depth of intermediate and centre chronograph wheels so deep, by means of the eccentric plug on to which the lever carrying the intermediate wheel banks, as actually to stop the whole watch running and then to turn the plug until the train starts to run and a full arc of vibration of the balance is obtained. It is said then that the correct depth is made. It is true that this depth should be as deep as possible so as to minimise the backlash of the centre chronograph wheel in order that the tension spring shall be as light as possible. But it is to be preferred, and is safer, that the depth should be *seen*, as already noted. Let the chronograph run, under close observation of the depth, for at least one minute, to ensure that there is no " bad depth," due, perhaps, to want of truth in the round of one of the wheels.

When satisfied with this part of the test, pay attention to the minute counter mechanism. As the finger piece comes round to move the intermediate minute counter wheel, see that it enters between the two teeth freely. The point of the finger piece must be free of the preceding tooth and it should travel round and move the wheel one tooth so that the head of the jumper spring is lifted up and over one tooth and the tension of that spring will complete the operation, the wheel will jump one tooth. As the finger piece is about to enter between two teeth, stop the balance with a pointed piece of pegwood. Then move the balance backward and forward so that the action of the finger piece can be observed accurately. See the finger enter, move round and touch the outgoing tooth and move it, observe the head of the jumper spring lift and the end of the tooth of the minute counter wheel pass under it ; then to the finger piece again and see it about to disconnect and then the jumper spring take charge and move the wheel one tooth. This action is most important ; many chronographs stop because of a faulty minute counter action and it is worth some close attention.

Several faults can occur here. It may be that the finger piece butts on the end of the preceding tooth before entry or the finger may move the wheel too far. If the jumper is adjustable, move the minute counter wheel round a little so that the finger enters freely and then observe as it disconnects. If the disconnecting is correct it indicates that the cure was with the jumper but if the finger moves the wheel too far it points to the fact that the finger is too long and must be shortened. On the other hand, if the intersection of the finger is shallow and it enters between two teeth freely but does not move the wheel far enough for the jumper to act, then the eccentric plug, upon which the intermediate counter wheel lever banks, must be turned to make it deeper. Should the entry of the finger be as deep as is safe, i.e. it just frees the preceding tooth but it does not move the wheel far enough the cure rests with the jumper as already explained.

It is necessary now to revert to the case where the jumper head was riding a tooth when the return to zero lever was pressing on the heart piece. First and foremost, the changing over of the minute counter must be correct and if this has been achieved by moving an adjustable jumper or by stoning one side of the head of the jumper, it must not be altered to accommodate the condition of the head riding a tooth when at zero. Sometimes the one correction if there is an error will correct both faults. If you are left with the head riding a tooth then this must be corrected by altering the angle of the head of the return to zero lever operating on the heart cam of the minute counter wheel. To cite a specific case, if the jumper is as in Fig. 101, then stone the head of the lever in the direction as dotted line (the illustration is exaggerated). This will have the effect of moving the wheel round slightly and allowing the head of the jumper spring to rest between two teeth.

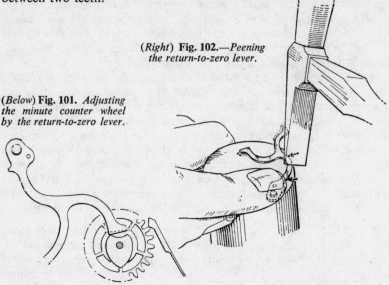

(*Right*) **Fig. 102.**—*Peening the return-to-zero lever.*

(*Below*) **Fig. 101.** *Adjusting the minute counter wheel by the return-to-zero lever.*

Start the chronograph running and observe, as the point of both heart cams rotate, that they are free of the heads of the return to zero lever. If they are not, then peen the side of the lever on the underside as shown in Fig. 102. Should the head operating upon the centre chronograph cam foul and the minute counter cam be free, the small amount necessary to " bend " the lever will not affect the minute counter cam materially. Hold the lever upside down on a flat steel stake in the vice and hammer with the peen of the hammer along the edge between the arrows (Fig. 102). The lever is held down flat but the peen strikes at an angle. Remove any bruises the hammer may have made by stroking with an Arkansas slip. There is a method of " stretching " the part of the lever operating upon the column wheel, but this is not satisfactory because the " stretching " really consists of knocking up a burr and this burr soon wears down and the original fault prevails.

Running Test

With the dial and hands fitted on to the movement, and it is more convenient with the movement fitted into its case with the button and shaft in, make the following test.

Start the chronograph running and observe the actual start of the chronograph hand to see that it does not jump, as already explained. Then as the hand comes up to the 60 seconds observe when the minute counter starts to move. To be correct it should not move until after the chronograph hand has passed the 60 seconds mark. There should be no appreciable lapse ; less than one-fifth of a second. The counter hand should not move at 58 or 59 seconds, but at the moment after reaching 60 seconds. To correct, if faulty, move the finger piece round slightly on the chronograph arbor. Hold the wheel in the fingers and twist the finger piece with brass-lined pliers in the desired direction.

If all the points described have been carefully attended to then, when starting, the hand should " step " forward smoothly ; the minute counter hand should start to move immediately after 60 seconds and should complete its movement in under one second. When the chronograph mechanism is stopped the chronograph hand should stop dead—no slight movement backward or a slight jump forward ; the return to zero should be decisive and both hands should fly back to zero smartly and dead on to the 60 seconds mark in the case of the chronograph hand and to the 30-minute mark the minute counter hand (or to the zero mark, the minute counter may be 15, 45 or 60 minutes).

Finally, complete the oiling. Apply a little watch oil to the top pivots of the centre chronograph and minute counter wheels ; a trace of watch oil to the head of the minute counter jumper spring ; just grease with clock oil the faces of the heads of the return to zero lever, so that the edges of the two heart cams are slightly greased ; a little clock oil to the blocks of the column wheel.

Vital Points in Repair

Important points concerning all chronographs :—

The teeth of chronograph wheels must be cleaned with a glass brush.

The depth of the intermediate chronograph into the centre chronograph wheel must be correct.

The operation of the minute wheel counter by the finger piece must be correct.

The chronograph hand must fit tightly and be placed into position —with the return to zero lever on the heart cams—pointing *exactly* to the 60 mark, not even the thickness of a one-fifth second mark off. Sometimes if the hand is a hairs'-breath off, the hand can be " stroked " into position. With brass tweezers stroke the hand in the direction required, as indicated in Fig. 103. The bend, an

81

extremely slight curve, is not
discernible to the eye. On no
account should the hand be
bent so much that the bend is
obvious; in these circumstances
it is better to remove the hand
and fit again.

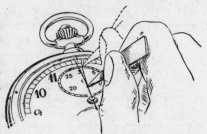

With the chronograph
running, and the watch held
close to the ear, you should
be able to hear the chronograph

Fig. 103.—*Stroking the chronograph hand
into position.*

" sing," i.e. a slight ringing noise owing to vibration of the chronograph hand.

I have discussed, at some length, perhaps, what may appear to
be trivial points, but all of them are vital to the correct functioning of
a chronograph. They are the fundamental adjustments of all chronographs, split-second chronographs and timers.

Wrist Chronograph Systems

The majority of chronographs passing through the workshops
to-day are wrist watches and most of these are on the two push-piece
system (Fig. 104). This calibre, with column wheel, is made by the

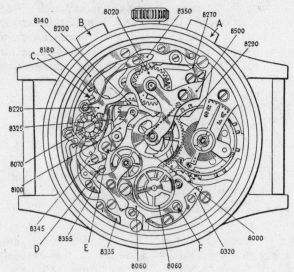

Fig. 104.—*The column wheel wrist
chronograph.*

Fig. 105.—*Symbol by which
the above chronograph may
be recognised (Valjoux).
13''' V.Z. 23.*

Ebauches factory, Valjoux, S.A. of Les Bioux, Switzerland. It will be found in various standards of finish, i.e. qualities, according to the finishing factory who handle it and they, in all probability, will give the movement a name. The push-piece *A* starts the chronograph train running and a second push on the same piece will stop it.

A second push on the push-piece *A* will start the chronograph running again from where it was stopped ; the hands will not have returned to zero. This can be an advantage where an intermittent recording is required, such as to check the time of flow of liquid. The flow starts and the chronograph is set into action, then there is a hold-up in the flow, maybe to fill another container, and the chronograph is stopped. The flow starts again and the chronograph is set into action. In this manner the amount of liquid used—the rate of flow is known —can be ascertained without calculation.

A push on *B* will return the hands to zero. Other than the two-push pieces and the additional lever *C* the mechanism is exactly similar to the one already described. The calibre is also made with one-push piece, i.e. triple action from the one-push piece.

The screw heads of the plugs *D*, *E* and *F* are eccentric and control the depth of action of the levers bearing upon them. They should not be moved during dismantling and cleaning, but they may have to be turned when adjusting, as already explained.

The manufacturers recommend the following order of assembly. The numbers given to the parts are those of Ebauches S.A., Neuchâtel, Switzerland, to whom we are indebted for the illustrations of this model and the two calibres which follow. If a new part is required it is necessary to quote the number only, which in this case is 13‴ V.Z.23. Irrespective of the name on the movement, the calibre can be recognised by the trade mark letter R in a shield as shown in Fig. 105.

Assembly of the Valjoux Chronograph

The order of assembly, and in reverse to dismantle, is as follows :—

1. The friction or tension spring 8290.

2. The intermediate minute counter wheel assembly 8100 and spring 8325.

3. Minute counter wheel 8020 and centre chronograph wheel 8000 and then the cock 8500.

4. The minute counter wheel jumper 8270.

5. The column wheel 8070 and its jumper spring 8355.

6. Return-to-zero push lever 8180 and start-stop lever 8140 and its spring 8335.

7. The brake lever 8200 and its spring 8345.

8. The intermediate lever assembly and its spring 8320.

9. The wheel fitted on to fourth wheel pivot 8060.

10. The return-to-zero lever 8220 and its spring 8350.

This factory recommends the oiling of all chronograph wheel pivots, with the exception of the minute counter wheel pivots and the intermediate minute counter wheel pivots. Finally, apply the tests as noted on page 75.

It is the common practice with all Swiss factories to indicate a left-hand screw by cutting two additional slots on the head. These are a lighter cut, on each side of the centre slot (Fig. 106).

Fig. 106.—*Slots in the head indicate a left-hand thread.*

Two-push Chronographs without Column Wheel

The two-push chronograph without column wheel shown in Fig. 107 is made by Le Landeron, of Le Landeron, Switzerland. The trade mark or sign of this factory is the letter L in a shield as shown in Fig. 108 and as with the Valjoux, the movement, no matter what name has been given to it, can be recognised by this sign.

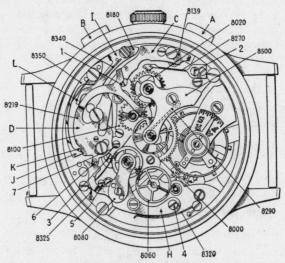

Fig. 107.—*The two-push chronograph without column wheel.*

Fig. 108.—*Symbol by which the chronograph may be recognised (Le Landeron). 13¾''' 48.*

There is no column wheel. The push *A* starts the chronograph running and the push *B* stops and returns to zero. The first push on *B* stops it and the second push on *B* returns the hands to zero. The action is quite simple and is as follows :—

Push-piece *A* operates on the lever *C* and this lever engages in the slot of lever *D*. Fitted to this lever is the screw 6 and fixed to the lever 8100, which carries the intermediate minute counter wheel, is the screw 7; both screws 6 and 7 are not ordinary screws and they should not be turned. The screw 7 of the lever 8100 bears upon the lever *C* by virtue of its spring. The lever *H*, which carries the intermediate chronograph wheel, bears upon the screw 6 of the return-to-zero lever *D* so that when the lever *C* is depressed the lever *D* swivels upon its stud and is drawn away from the centre and at the same time the lever 8100 draws from the centre and the lever *H* drops towards the centre. Thus the return-to-zero lever and the intermediate counter lever are drawn from the centre chronograph wheel and the intermediate chronograph wheel engages with the centre chronograph wheel and the mechanism is set into motion. To stop the chronograph running, the lever *I* is depressed when the push *B* is used. This lever depresses the lever *C* which in turn moves the lever *D*. This lever is controlled by the jumper spring *J* working in the notches *K* and one press of the push *B* allows one notch to pass, sufficient movement has been given to the lever *D* to disconnect the gears of the chronograph wheels and consequently the centre chronograph wheel stops. Upon releasing the push *M* the lever *I* returns to its normal position by virtue of its spring. By this time the lever *D* is in such a position that upon a second push of the push-piece *B*, the end of the lever *I* at *L* is able to press the lever *D* down and by reason of the jumper action it snaps home and returns the heart pieces to zero. It is a most ingenious piece of designing, simple and definite in action.

The screw heads marked 1 to 7 are not ordinary screws, they are eccentric plugs and should not be moved. They are used when it is necessary to adjust a depth or change of position of the part bearing upon them.

Assembly of the Landeron Chronograph

The numbers in the illustration (Fig. 107) are the numbers given to the parts by the Ebauche manufacturer, and when ordering a new piece it is necessary to give the number only and the calibre name and number.

The order of assembly, and in reverse to dismantle, is as follows :—

1. The tension spring 8290.

2. The intermediate minute counter wheel 8100 and its spring 8325.

3. The minute recording wheel 8020 the centre chronograph wheel 8000, and then the chronograph cock 8500.

4. The minute recorder wheel jumper 8270.

5. The starting lever 8139.

6. The return-to-zero push lever 8219.

7. Stop return-to-zero push lever 8180.

8. The springs 8340 and 8350.

9. The intermediate chronograph wheel lever assembly 8080 and its spring 8320.

10. The wheel fitted to fourth wheel pivot 8060.

Finally apply the tests as noted on page 75.

The chronograph shown in Fig. 109 is, like that shown in Fig. 107, a two-push-piece model without column wheel. The ébauche is made by Venus S.A., Moutier, Switzerland, and can be recognised by the sign of a star in the shield as shown in Fig. 110, no matter what name has been given to the movement. The design is however different to the Le Landeron described. The push A starts and stops the chronograph running and push-piece B returns to zero.

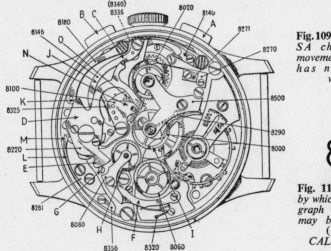

Fig. 109.—*The Venus SA chronograph movement which has no column wheel.*

Fig. 110.—*Symbol by which the chronograph on the left may be recognised (Venus).* CAL. 14''' 188.

The action is as follows :—

Pressing the push A depresses the lever C and the end of this operates on a cam with a part shaped like ∧. The first plunge takes place on the left-hand side of the $\wedge$ and it causes the return-to-zero lever D to draw away from the centre, and at the same time, the end of the lever E releases the lever F, where the screw G, fixed to the lever F, has been resting on the lever D at E. This movement allows the intermediate chronograph wheel H to gear into the centre chronograph wheel I and so the chronograph mechanism starts to run. Another push on the push-piece A and the end of the lever C presses upon the other side of the $\wedge$ shaped part, because the point of this part has been brought to the left side of the lever C by reason of the first push. The lever D is therefore pushed towards the centre and in so doing the end E contacts the screw G and pushes the lever F away from the centre and the intermediate chronograph wheel is disconnected from the centre chronograph wheel and the chronograph mechanism stops.

When the piece B is depressed the pin of the lever J contacts the lever D at K and pushes it towards the centre and the two ends return the heart-piece to zero. Also at the same time, the lever N carrying the intermediate minute counter wheel O is drawn away from the centre and therefore the finger-piece fitted to the centre chronograph wheel is disconnected with the intermediate counter wheel. The snap effect is obtained by the jumper spring L operating upon the notches at M cut into the $\wedge$ cam and fixed to the lever D.

Fig. 111.—*The Venus S.A. chronograph indicating the eccentric pins.*

The screw heads 1 to 4 (Fig. 111) are eccentric plugs and should not be turned ; they are for adjusting the depth, etc., of the parts bearing upon them.

The numbers notes in the illustration (Fig. 109) are the numbers given to the parts by the ébauche manufacturer, and when ordering a new part quote the number only and the calibre name and number.

Assembly of the Venus Chronograph

The order of assembly, and in reverse to dismantle, is as follows :—

1. The lever spring 8335 and the plate 8281.

2. The tension spring 8290.

3. The intermediate minute counter wheel assembly 8100 and its spring 8325.

4. The minute counter wheel 8020 and the centre chronograph wheel 800 and then the chronograph cock 8500.

4. The minute counter wheel jumper spring 8270.

6. The stop-start lever 8140 and the lever 8180 and the lever 8146.

7. The return-to-zero lever 8220 and then the jumper spring 8356.

8. Check action of stop-start lever 8146 through hole in lever 8220.

9. The intermediate chronograph wheel assembly 8080 and its spring 8320.

10. The wheel fitted to pivot of fourth wheel 8060.

Finally apply the tests as noted on page 75.

Chronograph Dials

The uses to which chronographs can be put are almost legionary. Various calculations are made and the dial calibrated so that the user himself has no need to make calculations ; all he has to do is to select the chronograph with the dial to suit his purpose, " press the button," and the *exact* answer is shown on the dial. The main dials of different calibrations are illustrated here, and they form a useful reference. But the dials shown are not the complete range, if the dials of timers are included. Later on timers will be described and a range of dials illustrated.

Fig. 112.—*Minute recording chronograph ;* On the outside is the 1/5th of a second circle. *A* is the minute counter and *B* three-minute divisions to time the length of telephone conversations.

Fig. 113.—*Hour recording chronograph ;* In addition to the minute counter dial with the timing of telephone conversations, is the dial between 7 and 5, calibrated to record hours, up to 12.

Fig. 114.—*Tachometer chronograph ;* The word " tachometer " is from the Greek " Takhus," swift.   The tachometer circle is calibrated to record the speed of a moving object, such as a motor car, aeroplane, etc., over a known distance.   The standard distance upon which the calibration is made is shown on the dial as " Base 1,000 metres," or

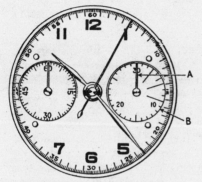

Fig. 112.—*Minute Recording.*

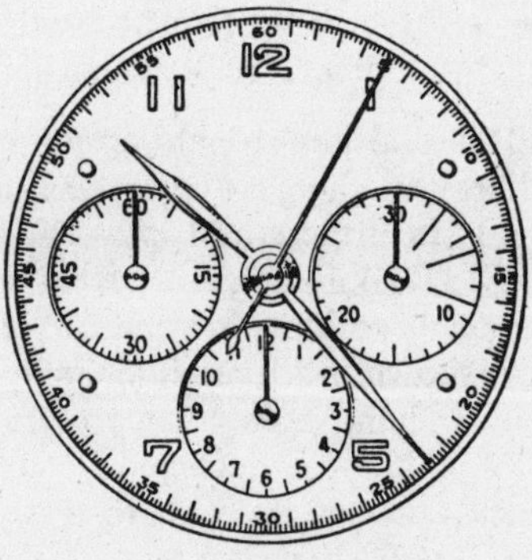

Fig. 113.—*Hour Recording.*

" Base 1 mile," etc.   The push to start the chronograph running is pressed as the object to be timed passes the starting point, and the hand is stopped when it reaches the finishing point.   The chronograph hand will then indicate the speed in miles or metres per hour.

Fig. 115.—*Telemeter chronograph ;* The word " telemeter " is from the Greek " Tele," far off, at a distance.   The telemeter circle, outside the seconds scale, is calibrated to measure the distance an object, or a phenomenon, is from the observer, provided the object is visible and audible.   The calibration is based upon the speed of sound through the air, i.e. approximately 1,115 feet or 340 metres per second.

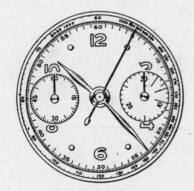

Fig. 114.—*Tachometer.*

Fig. 115.—*Telemeter.*

If, for instance, the chronograph is started when the observer sees the flash from a gun, and then stops it when he hears the report, the chronograph hand will then record the distance of the gun from the observer in miles or kilometres, according to how the dial is calibrated. Similarly, if the chronograph hand is started when a flash of lightning is observed, and stopped when the thunder is heard the hand will indicate the distance of the storm from the observer, since lightning and thunder are simultaneous.

This dial is also calibrated as a tachometer, *A*. With this form of calibration the reading is as follows. If the minute recording hand points to 0 the speed is as shown in the outer circle, i.e. between 60 and 1,000 kilometres. If the minute counter points to one minute, i.e. one complete revolution of the chronograph hand, the reading is as shown in the middle circle, between 30 and 60, and if the minute counter hand points to two numbers, then the reading is as shown on the inner circle between 30 and 20. Therefore, if the object being timed takes 60 seconds to travel 1 kilometre it will be travelling at a speed of 60 Km. per hour ; if it takes 2 minutes, 30 Km. per hour ; and 3 minutes, 20 Km. per hour. This particular tachometer scale is marked in kilometres and intended for a 1 kilometre base, but it will serve the same purpose for a 1 mile base, and the scale readings should then be taken as miles. The base can, in fact, be any unit distance, and the scale read off in the same units.

Fig. 116.—*Pulsimeter chronograph ;* the circle indicated on the edge of this chronograph dial is calibrated for the purpose of pulse taking. The chronograph is started when the counting begins and at the 16th beat (or after 15 beats) the chronograph is stopped. The reading on the scale gives the number of pulse beats per minute. Dials are calibrated also to take 30 and 20 beats.

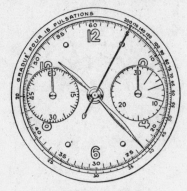 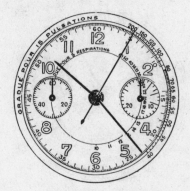

Fig. 116.—*Pulsimeter.*   **Fig. 117.—*Asthmometer.***

Fig. 117.—*Asthmometer chronograph ;* The word " asthmometer " is taken from the Greek " Asthma," panting. The chronograph is started as the respirations are counted, and upon the expirations of the 5th, 10th, 15th, 20th and 25th respiration, according to the basis of calibration indicated on the dial, the chronograph is stopped. The reading on the scale indicated by the hand then shows the number of respirations per minute.

Fig. 118.—*Production-counting chronograph ;* The object of this scale, on the outer edge, is to determine the number of articles or operations, produced per hour. The production circle is calibrated so that if the hand is started at the beginning of the production of an article, or of an operation, and stopped upon completion, the reading will give the number of articles or operations per hour. This statement is correct provided that the time is more than 5 seconds and less than 60 seconds. If the time is less than 5 seconds it is necessary to take as a basis several observations and multiplying the number

(*Below*) **Fig. 118.**—*Production Counter.*

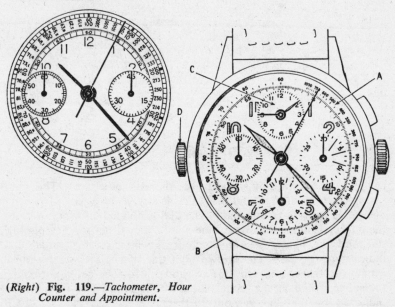

(*Right*) **Fig. 119.**—*Tachometer, Hour Counter and Appointment.*

of observations by the number shown on the scale. Should the production take longer than 60 seconds, then the time recorded will, of course, have to be divided into 60 minutes to give the rate of production per hour.

Fig. 119.—*Appointment or memento dial chronograph ;* In addition to the tachometer scale, *A*, and an hour counter up to 12 hours, *B*, there is the dial *C*, where the hands are set by the button *D*, which forms a reminder of an appointment or event.

Fig. 120.—*Multiple-purpose chronograph ;* This dial is calibrated with tachometer scale *A*, telemeter scale *B*, pulsimeter scale *C*, and minute counter, *D*, with 3-minute divisions for duration of telephone conversations.

Fig. 121.—*Tide chronograph ;* The dial *A* is divided into 5-minute sections for the purpose of yachting. It gives at a glance the duration

(*Below*) **Fig. 120.** — *Multiple-Purpose.*

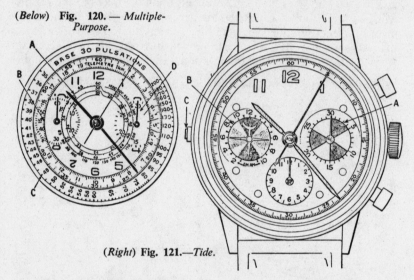

(*Right*) **Fig. 121.**—*Tide.*

of the 5-minute warning signal before the start of a race. The dial *B* shows the time of high and low tides at any given place. The push-piece *C* is for setting this dial. The dial is divided into four sections, the darker sections (coloured blue on the actual dial) indicating high tide and the lighter sections (coloured yellow on the actual dial) indicating low tide. The known high tide of a place is ascertained, usually at the coastguard station, and the dial is set accordingly ; thereafter, while in the same place, the high and low tides will be indicated by the dial without further reference to the coastguard station.

Fig. 122.—*Chronograph with centre minute counter hand ;* In place of the normal minute counter dial, the hand *A* records the minutes up to 60 on the scale *B*.

Fig. 123.—*Direction-finding chronograph ;* The hand *A* is first set to the known North with the aid of a compass by the button *B*. This hand rotates once in 24 hours. Thereafter if the watch is held horizontally with the hour hand pointing towards the sun the hand *A* will point to the North. In addition, the seconds hand *C* can be set to the exact second by pushing in the button *D* and turning, useful when it is required to set the watch to the exact second given by a time signal.

(Below) **Fig. 122.**—*Centre Minute Counter.*

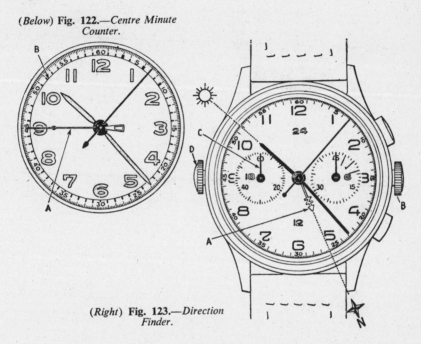

(Right) **Fig. 123.**—*Direction Finder.*

The calculating watch ; Although the calculating watch is not a chronograph, or even a complicated watch, it should be put on record for its ingenuity. Made by Juvenia of La Chaux-de-Fonds, Switzerland, it is in fact, a slide rule, made in a circular form, and can be used for all purposes to which a slide rule is put ; multiplication, division, finding roots and powers, etc. The illustration Fig. 124 gives the general appearance of the watch and Figs. 125 to 127 show how it operates.

(1) To set. Turn the bezel clockwise until the pointer stops at 12 noon and then continue turning, until the multiplicand or the devisor appears in the radius of the pointer. Fig. 125—The figure 35 has been set.

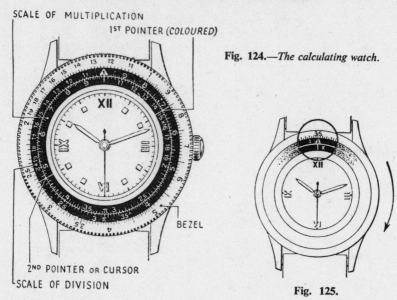

SCALE OF MULTIPLICATION
1ST POINTER (*COLOURED*)

BEZEL

2ND POINTER OR CURSOR
SCALE OF DIVISION

Fig. 124.—*The calculating watch.*

Fig. 125.

(2) To multiply. Turn the bezel anti-clockwise until pointer and multiplicand reach the multiplier, e.g. multiplying by 5. Fig. 126— $35 \times 5 = 175$.

(3) To divide, use the other scale. Read the result as shown in Fig. 127, $35 + 5 \div 7$.

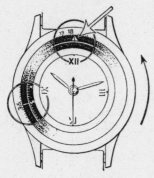

Fig. 126.

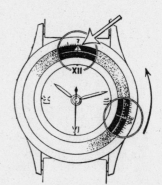

Fig. 127.

Split Seconds Chronograph

The split seconds chronograph is so called because the seconds hands divide or split. This is, of course, not strictly true because in fact one hand is superimposed upon the other ; there are two hands so that two records of time can be registered. The usual action is

94

that when the chronograph mechanism is started the two hands rotate together as one. Upon depressing the split seconds push piece, one hand stops and the other continues to rotate. When the split push is depressed again the split seconds hand catches up the normal chronograph hand and again travels with it. Therefore the seconds are not split ; if the train is an 18,000 one the seconds hands will indicate one-fifth seconds and there is no means of dividing that on this particular watch. The seconds hands themselves split or divide. The name, though cumbersome, should be " Dividing seconds hands watch."

The action is quite simple and is as follows :—In addition to the normal chronograph column wheel is another similar wheel which can be made to rotate by the lever *A* (Fig. 128) and is controlled by the jumper spring *B*. Operating upon the upper set of the teeth of the column wheel *C* is the pair of levers *D* which together have a pincer-like appearance. The handle-like end of the pincers is made to grip the periphery of a very light wheel *E* by reason of the springs *F*. Fitted to the arbor of the centre chronograph wheel is a heart piece *G*. Pivoted on to the wheel *E* is the lever *H* which carries the roller *I*. In a high-

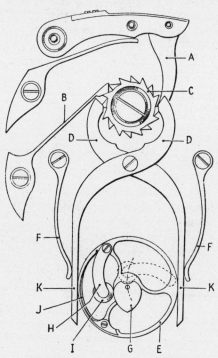

grade watch the roller is made of synthetic ruby or sapphire. The spring *J* bears upon the lever *H* and keeps it into close contact with the heart piece. The periphery of the wheel *E* is very finely serrated, not actually with teeth, but roughened. The inside of the levers *D* are similarly roughened at *K*.

With the chronograph running and the split seconds wheel held firmly, the heart piece *G* will rotate and push the roller *I* away so that it will ride up and down upon the edge. If the jaws of the pincer-like levers are opened by reason of the teeth of the column wheel pushing them out, the wheel *E* will be released and free, and the lever *H*, pressing

Fig. 128.—*Split-seconds mechanism.*

95

on to the heart piece, will be made to return to its zero position as shown by the dotted line outline of the lever and roller, which is at the base of the heart piece.

Fitted to the wheel E is a long pipe and it is to this pipe the split seconds hand is fitted. When the split seconds wheel is free the chronograph and split seconds hands are together, i.e. one over the other, the split seconds hand below the chronograph hand. When the split wheel is gripped by the levers the split hand stops, while the chronograph hand goes on.

With a movement of a lower grade, a lever somewhat similar to the return to zero lever is employed in place of the jewel roller. But whatever the alterations in design as a form of economy in production —the levers D may be two separate levers working one upon each side of the column wheel—the principle is as has been explained.

General Notes

The split seconds mechanism must be light in action and therefore it is delicate. No oil at all should be used on the split seconds wheels, i.e. on the pivots of the wheel, the roller, the lever or the heart piece ; all these light moving parts should be left quite dry. To oil them would cause dragging. The column wheel, pivoting of the pincer-like levers, and where the spring impinges upon the levers should be oiled in the normal manner.

The fitting of the hands needs careful and close attention. First place the split hand on to its pipe in the *exact* zero position and then the chronograph hand also *exactly* in position. For the split seconds hands to be correct it should not be possible to see the split hand at all when viewing down upon the hands. In this instance the hands must not be " stroked " into position, as advised when dealing with the single chronograph. When the hands are viewed from the side, they should be perfectly parallel. The adjustment of the hands of a split second chronograph needs very careful attention indeed. It is work that cannot be hurried. It may be observed that the seconds chronograph hand appears to work forward after the chronograph action has been operated several times, this may be due to the hand itself not being hard enough, the return to zero is relatively violent and the sudden jerk jolts the hand and bends it, the temper of the hand is not good enough to straighten out. The remedy is to change the hand for one of better temper and more spring like.

Section 3

TIMERS

Technically, the timer is distinct from the chronograph inasmuch as it is not intended to tell the time of day but to record short intervals of time.

Generally, the mechanism of the timer is so constructed that the seconds hand is fitted direct on to the pipe of the heart piece and this cam is fitted friction-tight on to the arbor of what is virtually the centre wheel of the movement ; there is no continuously running train, as where the centre seconds-hand is brought into action by the operation of bringing another train of wheels into gear. The seconds-hand of a timer is, as a rule, directly driven.

There is, however, an exception to this rule. A timer is made which employs the conventional chronograph mechanism with a continuous running train, and such timers are usually fitted with an off-set seconds hand which rotates continuously and is independent of the chronograph work. Although such instruments have chronograph mechanisms they are still defined as timers because they do not record the time of day.

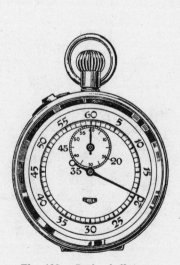

Fig. 129.—*Basket ball timer.*

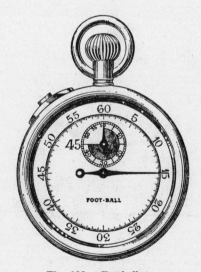

Fig. 130.—*Football timer.*

97

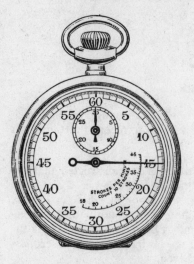

Fig. 131.—*Rowing and sculling timer.*

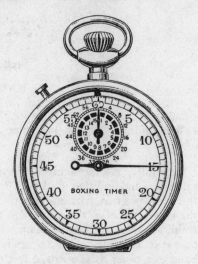

Fig. 132.—*Boxing timer.*

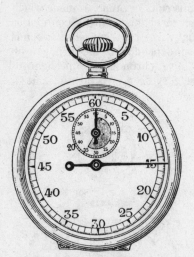

Fig. 133.—*Ice hockey timer.*

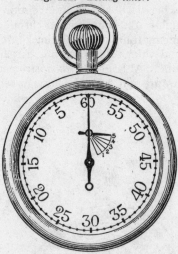

Fig. 134.—*Yachting timer.*

Timers are made to record 1/5th, 1/10th, 1/20th, 1/30th, 1/50th and 1/100th of a second. Generally speaking, timers will run at each full winding of the mainspring for the time as follows :—

1/5th	..	..	..	..	$10\frac{1}{2}$ hours
1/10th	..	..	..	..	$5\frac{1}{2}$,,
1/20th	..	..	..	..	$5\frac{1}{2}$,,

1/30th	..	..	..	..	3	„
1/50th	..	..	..	..	3	„
1/100th	..	..	..	..	30 minutes	

Timers made with 12-hour recording dials will go for 15 hours with one winding.

Fig. 135.—*Water polo timer.*

As with chronographs, the dials of timers are calibrated for a great number of purposes and they include, as illustrated on these pages, basket ball, boxing, football, hockey, ice hockey, sculling, water polo, yachting. In addition to the dials illustrated here, they are calibrated as most of the chronograph dials illustrated on pages 89–93.

In fact the dial can be calibrated for almost any conceivable purpose, sport or scientific.

The Movement

As the fundamental principle of all timers is similar—with the exception of the continuously running, which has been described under Chronographs —one model only will be described here. The illustrations in Figs. 136 and 137 show a typical example. We are indebted to Lemania Watch Co., of Orient, Switzerland, for these illustrations.

The mechanism is perfectly simple but. there are certain points to watch in order to obtain the best results. The action will be described first.

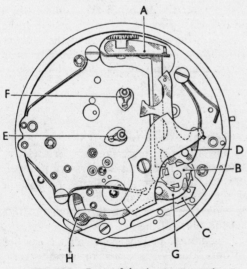

Fig. 136.—*Parts of the timer movement.*

99

The start, stop and return to zero are actuated from the one push piece, the winding button. The train consists of the barrel geared to a pinion, the extended arbor of which carries the minute counter heart piece to which is fitted the minute counter hand. The wheel fixed to the pinion gears into the pinion of what is in a normal watch the centre pinion. On the extended arbor of this pinion is the seconds heart piece and to the pipe of the heart piece the seconds hand is fitted. The wheel fixed to the seconds pinion gears into the escape wheel pinion.

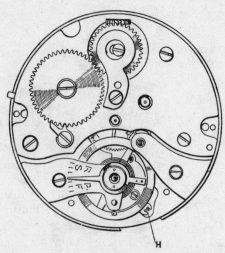

Fig. 137.—*Timer movement showing the balance and pin for holding it up.*

When the push piece *A* (Fig. 136) is depressed it causes the column wheel *B* to step round ; this is controlled by the jumper spring *C*. The first push lifts the return to zero lever *D* free of the heart pieces *E* and *F* and they are now free to rotate, but it is not until the stop *H* on the balance lever *G* drops off the block of the column wheel that the balance is free, and the heart pieces can, in fact, rotate. The second push operates the stop on the balance lever and the balance is stopped. The third push allows the return to zero lever to drop smartly between the blocks on the column and so contact the heart pieces and return them to the zero position.

Repair

When dismantling the movement it may be found that the hands are fitted abnormally tightly and, in such circumstances, it is advisable not to remove them ; it is not essential unless it is necessary to repair a heart piece, such as to fit a new tension spring. Simply remove the dial, with the hands and heart pieces. If the hands cannot be removed, then clean the heart pieces, while they are attached to the dial, with a clean, dry brush and see that the edges of the heart pieces are perfectly clean. Peg the holes with a long pointed peg sharpened almost parallel. The pipes fit on to their arbors loosely ; the tension springs, only, grip the arbors. Use the bellows liberally to ensure perfect freedom

100

from dust both in the holes of the pipes and between the dial and the heart pieces. Other than this contingency the movement is dismantled and cleaned in the conventional manner.

Assembly

Having assembled the train and the escapement, it is convenient to place the movement in its case to assemble the stopwork mechanism. As the mechanism is so simple and in view of the information contained in the chapter on Chronographs it is not necessary to give the assembly in detail, so oiling and adjustment alone will be considered.

Apply a little clock oil to the nick turned in the arbors of both the seconds arbor and the minute counter arbor. Apply clock oil to all the active surfaces of the stopwork mechanism. When testing the action, greater control can be exercised if the watch is held as in Fig. 138. The button can then be pushed in slowly so that the action of the various levers can be observed closely. It is important that the return to zero lever is lifted free, of the heart pieces first and then the stop on the balance lever operates. It will be noted that the pin H (Figs. 136 and 137) contacting the balance describes an arc and so moves the balance to ensure that it shall start vibrating directly it is released ; it must not stop as the result of the escapement setting. It is necessary, therefore, to see that the escapement is in perfect beat, otherwise there may be a point, owing to repeated stopping and starting, after very short intervals of running, where the balance will not start to vibrate upon being released, it will not have had sufficient time for the arc of vibration of the balance to pick up.

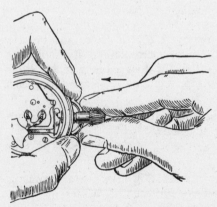

Fig. 138.—*Holding a timer to check the action.*

If the hands were not removed when the movement was dismantled, set the return to zero lever in the position free of the heart piece before replacing the dial. When the dial is in position and the heart pieces pressed home, try the friction tension of the hands. Move the hands with a fine oiler. They should be sufficiently tight to grip their arbors ; if they are not then the hands must be removed, so to adjust the tension spring.

If the heart pieces are placed in position before the dial then make this test before fitting the hands. If there is any doubt about the hands being tight enough, remove the small tension spring and close it in slightly so that it bears harder upon the arbor.

Now to refit the hands, if they were removed. They must fit very tightly. The tension of the return to zero lever spring is strong, and the impact of the lever with the heart pieces could dislodge the hands if they were not fitted tightly. After removal of the hands it may be found necessary to close the hole slightly to ensure a tight fit. Having pressed the hand on to the heart piece pipe as firmly as possible with the back of the handle of a watch brush, give the hand a sharp single blow with a hammer to drive home. Usually there is no shoulder on to which the heart pieces rest and, if they are pressed hard enough, the underside of the heart piece contacts the plate of the movement so, usually, it is quite safe to give a blow within reason, in most cases sufficient to drive the hand hard home.

The testing of the hand work is similar to that of the chronograph— already described. The seconds hand should not move until the balance is released and then it should step forward smoothly. The minute counter hand moves so slowly that it is not our first concern ; concentrate on the seconds hand. If this hand does move slightly and then stops it may be due to the heart piece tension not being strong enough, or the stop in the balance lever dropping off too soon. If the latter is the case the nose of the lever should be stretched a little so to delay the drop off. Another fault could be that the pin contacting the balance is bent, so that it leaves the balance too soon. The lever to which this pin is fitted has, of necessity, a larger radius than the balance and the remedy is to bend the pin towards the balance.

Occasionally, fortunately not frequently, one meets with a timer where one of the arbors persistently breaks off, usually the minute counter arbor. The cure is to remove the heart piece and observe the position of the nose of the return to zero lever ; it should just reach to the arbor but not touch it. If it does actually touch, stone the nose away with an Arkansas slip, retaining the same form, then well burnish it.

As mentioned before, there are many variations of this mechanism but the fundamental principle is the same.

Split Seconds Timers

The split seconds mechanism of timers is, in principle, the same as the split seconds chronograph explained in the last chapter.

Section 4

24 HOUR DIALS

Navigator Watch

The navigator watch made by Tissot, of Le Locle, Switzerland, is entitled to a space in these notes because of its dial. The purpose is to ascertain the time in various parts of the world, and at the same time, to show the time of day in the conventional manner. The watch is self-winding, and is fitted into a waterproof case.

The hour hand rotates once in 12 hours and local time is indicated on the outer zone A (Fig. 139). The inner chapter ring B (Fig. 140) is divided into 24 hours and the inner dial C is marked with the principal main cities in the 24 time zones. The inner dial, upon which these are printed, rotates once in 24 hours and is driven in a similar manner to the hands. The name representing each of the 24 time zones thus automatically appears opposite a particular figure of the chapter ring B . It is therefore quite simple to ascertain the time in any part of the world, provided that the watch has been set correctly and the time is read off the 24-hour dial B.

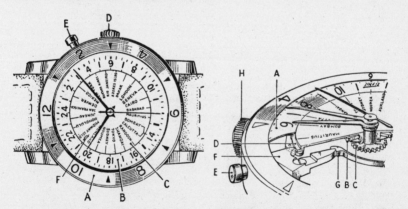

Fig. 139.—*The navigator watch.*   Fig. 140.—*Part section of the 24-hour ring and the time-zone dial.*

To set, withdraw the winding button D. By turning, the dial C will rotate as well as the hands. The time zone in which you are situated is set opposite the local time of day on the 24-hour dial, taking no notice of the position of the watch hands. Next, the push piece E is depressed. This locks the dial C so that it is possible to set the hands to the correct local time in the normal manner.

Therefore, if the time in London is 12 noon and the dial *C* and the hands are set to 12 o'clock, the time in New York will be 7 a.m. and in Calcutta 6 p.m. as indicated on the chapter ring *B*.

When returning the winding button, the push piece *E* is automatically released and the dial *C* is then free.

When travelling from one time zone to another, the button *D* is withdrawn and the hands set in the usual manner. The dial *C* will automatically be rotated to its correct position. If travelling from London to New York, for example, the hands, together with the dial *C* are set as shown by the ship's clocks, making sure to return the button upon completion. If travelling by air, then the hands must be set back the 5 hours at one setting and the dial *C* will automatically be set to its correct position.

The mark *F*, indicates the date line, so that if travelling between Auckland and Midway, this will remind you to note that the day of the month also has been changed. For instance, a traveller proceeding eastward to the Antipodes will anticipate the sun by 12 hours ; another travelling westward will be 12 hours behind time. The Aleutian Islands and Alaska come into the same dating as Australia and New Zealand.

To Dismantle

The zone *A* snaps on like an ordinary bezel and it is not necessary to remove it during the repair of the movement. The movement is removed from its case in the conventional manner. Particular care should be exercised in removing the hands ; the surface of the dial is delicate and it could not be restored unless it is returned to the factory. Place a fairly stout piece of paper—notepaper answers well—on each side of the hands for the hand levers to rest upon and lift the hands off slowly and carefully as explained in " Practical Watch Repairing."

The 24-hour ring *A* (Fig. 140) is held in position by two grub screws. Remove this ring and the centre dial can be lifted off. Fitted to the

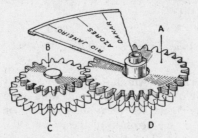

Fig. 141.—*Driving mechanism of the time-zone dial.*

centre dial is the wheel *B* which is held in position by the locking spring *C*. It will be noted that the centre dial is held in position by the zone *A* overlapping the step *D*. When the push *E* is depressed the nose of the lever *F* contacts the periphery of the centre dial and so holds it firmly while the hands are being set to local time. The jumper spring *G* holds the lever *F* in position while it is acting as a brake. To release the brake the winding button *H* is depressed and the pull-out-piece contacts the lever *F* and pushes it to the neutral position.

The wheel *A* (Fig. 131) fitted to the centre dial, gears with the wheel *B* and this wheel is riveted to the wheel *C* which gears with the hour wheel *D*.

Assembly

The mechanism is perfectly simple and during assembly it should be noted that the centre dial is quite free of the 24-hour dial. The makers give the following advice :

" Verify the centre dial ; it must be free and well centred with relation to the zone dial. Side clearance of 2/100 of a mm. should exist between them."

The movement is oiled in the normal manner. Apply a little clock oil to the locking spring *C* (Fig. 140). No oil at all is applied to the step of the centre dial.

Section 5

ALARM WATCHES

Alarm wrist watches are coming more into favour and among the principal makes are LeCoultre, Roamer, Lanco, Pierce, Cyma, Favre-Leuba, Borel, Reusser, Nitella, Olma, Simex, Friedli, Fulton, Mediator, and Aerina.

That selected for examination is by the Vulcain Watch Co., of La Chaux-de-Fonds, Switzerland. They have a wrist watch they have named the " Cricket " no doubt because of the cricket-like noise it makes when the alarm is sounding. The fundamental principle of the alarm work is much the same as the ordinary alarm clock, but there are one or two refinements. The Vulcain was the first wrist alarm to be made.

To Set the Alarm

The movement is fitted with two barrels, one for the going train and the other for the alarm. The winding button is turned anti-clockwise to wind the alarm train. The minute and hour hands are set in the conventional manner by withdrawing the winding button. It will be found that the hands can be set in one direction only—forwards, by turning the winding button anti-clockwise.

To set the alarm hand, press the push piece A (Fig. 142). This will cause the winding button to withdraw and the alarm hand can be set by turning the winding button in a clockwise direction ; the alarm hand rotates in an anti-clockwise direction. If the winding button is turned in the opposite direction to that stated, both when setting

Fig. 142.—*The " Cricket " alarm watch.*

the hands or the alarm hand, it will be found to be quite free ; no contact is made with the mechanism. When the alarm hand has been set, press the winding button back into position and this will automatically release the alarm setting mechanism and the push piece *A* will jump outward into its normal position.

When the alarm mainspring is fully wound the alarm will sound for 25 seconds and, if desired, it may be stopped by pressing the push piece *A* half-way in. If the alarm spring is wound and it is desired not to use the alarm at all press the push piece *A* half-way in. This will cause the winding button to jut out half-way to the hands set position ; in this neutral position the winding button is free and idle and drives no gears. To make the alarm operate, press the winding button in, which releases the alarm and the push piece will jump outward. Also, if the alarm mainspring is not wound at all, pressing the push piece half-way in will prevent the hammer from striking the sounding piece. *On no account should the push piece* A *be pulled out manually :* it is operated through the winding button *only*. The alarm dial *B* is calibrated in 10-minute intervals to facilitate the accurate setting of the alarm.

Dismantling the Alarm Watch

With the movement from its case, remove the hands and the dial. Turn the spring locking piece *A* (Fig. 143) a little to the left and it will spring up and away from the wheel it has been holding friction tight. Then unscrew the two screws *B* and *C* and lift off the plate *D*. The alarm setting wheels *E* and *F* (Fig. 144) can now be removed and then the alarm wheel *G*. It will be noted that the wheel *H* (Fig. 145) has three square holes placed at unequal distances apart and from the

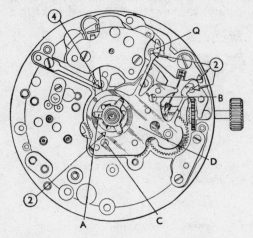

Fig. 143.—*Mechanism of the Vulcain alarm watch under the dial.*

OILING CHARTS
*Arrow 1—Watch oil (thin oil). Arrow 2—Clock oil (thick oil). Dotted Arrow 4—
Smear with clock oil underneath part.*

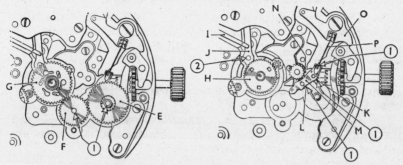

Fig. 144.—*Details of the alarm setting   Fig. 145.—The alarm setting mechanism.
mechanism.*

centre. These can coincide with three projections from the underside of the alarm wheel *G*, but in one position only will they coincide and allow the hour wheel *H* to spring upward, by virtue of the spring *I* pressing upon the lever *J*. The tailpiece of the lever is then free of the alarm pallets and allows the alarm to operate. The object of the three projections is to ensure that no side pressure is exerted upon the cannon pinion and by this means the hour wheel is able to rotate freely.

When setting the hands, the castle wheel engages the wheel *K*, and this wheel engages the wheel *L*, which is fitted to the rocking arm *M*, and when the winding button is made to rotate anti-clockwise, the wheel *N* engages the intermediate wheel, and so to the minute wheel and cannon pinion. If the winding button is made to rotate clockwise the wheel *L* is thrown out of gear and the button rotates freely.

When setting the alarm hand, the push piece *A*, Fig. 142, is depressed to its full extent and it contacts the lever *O*, Fig. 145, which forces the pull-out piece to the hand-set position and at the same time the spring *P* holds the rocking arm *M* to one side so that the wheel *M* engages the pinion of the wheel *E*, Fig. 144. This wheel engages the wheel *F*, which in turn engages the alarm wheel *G*. The lever *O* is held in position while setting the alarm by the check-spring *Q*, Fig. 143. It will be seen, therefore, that by depressing the alarm button the pull-out piece is automatically returned to its normal position.

Assembly

There are no special notes about the assembly. Oil as shown by the figures on Figs. 143-5, and refer to page 4 for the type of oil used. Other parts not indicated are oiled in the usual manner. It will be noted that the teeth of the crown and castle wheels are square in shape and not the conventional ratchet-shaped teeth.

An interesting innovation, patented by the Vulcain Watch Co., and introduced into this movement, is the shape of the balance end-stones. The jewel holes are olive shaped with flat tops and the end-stones are cone shaped (Fig. 146), the apex being off centre. The object is that when the movement is horizontal the staff pivots are pressed against the sides of the jewel holes and it is said that the friction so caused equalises the friction of the pivots bearing on the sides of the holes when the movement is in the vertical position. It is claimed that more accurate positional timing is obtained and that errors are reduced by as much as 50 per cent.

Fig. 146.—The cone-shaped endstones of the Vulcain alarm watch, showing the balance staff pivot bearing against one side of the jewel hole.

The unwary watch repairer may be tempted to reverse the endpieces, so to cause the pivots to bear on the flat surface of the endstones ; that would defeat the manufacturers' intention.

Section 6

CALENDAR WATCHES

Calendar watches may be divided into two classes : one where the date has to be altered when there are less than 31 days in the month, and the other where the number of days in the month is automatically controlled inasmuch as that the first of the month is always shown irrespective of the number of days in the month. The latter type is known as the " perpetual calendar."

Counting Types

Dealing first with the calendar which has to be changed when there are less than 31 days in the month, such calendars are really counting instruments similar to a car speedometer, where the number of miles travelled is recorded. Many watches are made to-day on which the date only is shown through an aperture or window in the dial. This mechanism is of the simplest order. A number of manufacturers do not provide a means of moving the date ring manually and, to set such watches to the correct date, the hands of the watch are turned until the correct date appears. There are, however, exceptions and the following is one.

The mechanism illustrated in Fig. 147 is typical and is made by Movado Watch Co., La Chaux-de-Fonds, Switzerland. It is Calibre No. 128.

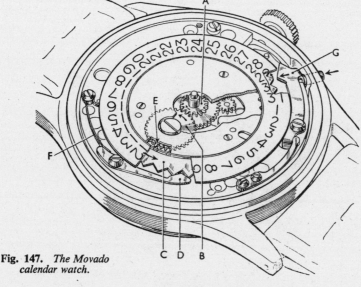

Fig. 147. *The Movado calendar watch.*

111

The wheel *A* of 16 teeth is mounted on to the hour wheel and gears with the wheel *B* of 32 teeth. This wheel has one extra-long tooth which contacts the triangular projections on the inside of the date ring *C*. This date ring has 31 such projections or teeth and also has 31 triangular teeth on its periphery. The jumper *D* controls the ring *C* as the tooth of the wheel *B* moves the ring—as shown at *E*—sufficiently for the apex of a tooth to press the nose of the jumper. The jumper then takes control and, by virtue of the spring *F*, causes the ring to complete its 1/31st of a turn. A disc with the date figures is mounted on to the ring *C*. To move the date ring round to its correct position, the jumper is depressed, and due to the position of its planting, the ring can be stepped backwards with the consequent forward projection of the number.

As with all calendar watches, when setting, the hands should be turned until the date has moved : this indicates midnight. Then set the hands to the correct time. For example, to set correctly on the 17th at 3 p.m., set the ring manually to the 16th, then turn the hands until the 17th appears and continue to turn the hands past noon and on to 3 o'clock.

The manufacturers recommend that the jumper should not be used when the date ring is about to be moved by the long tooth operating on the internal teeth of the ring as there would be a danger of injuring the long tooth.

Calendar with Moon Dial

Apply a little clock oil to the bearings of the jumper and the plunger and also where the springs make contact. Apply a little watch oil

Fig. 148.—*Omega " Cosmic " calendar watch.*

to the bearings of the wheel *B*, but no oil to the date ring. Grease the nose of the jumper with clock oil. The safest way to do this is to cut a piece of peg wood to chisel shape and then apply a little clock oil to it ; with this oily peg wipe the two surfaces of the nose of the jumper, move the ring round half-way and wipe again. There should be no free oil.

In the Omega " Cosmic " calendar watch (Cal. No. 381) shown in Fig. 148, the phases of the moon occupy one aperture, the days of the week another and the months of the year a third. The date is indicated by a long hand from the centre pointing to the scale of figures on the outer edge of the dial. The design is both good and simple, and there-fore the mechanism is trouble-free.

To dismantle, first remove the four hands in the conventional manner (with levers) taking the utmost care not to injure the dial. It is important not to mark *any* dial, but with complicated work such as this, it becomes even more important because it is impossible to get the dial restored, should it be marked, except by sending it to the factory in Switzerland. Having removed the hands, remove the dial and pack it in tissue paper and place in a safe place.

Lift the moon dial up and off its post. It is safe to lever up this dial and the calendar dials, having first removed the screws, with a piece of pegwood sharpened to a long chisel shape and then to lift the dials off with the fingers. Another method is to insert one blade of the tweezers under the dial so that when the other blade is closed it contacts the dial as near the centre as possible. Then with a steady hand lift the dial straight up and off ; make sure the tweezers do not move ; even a slight movement will mark the dial. The two calendar dials are first unscrewed before they can be lifted off.

To reiterate : it is good practice always to associate screws with their respective parts. In this instance the screws are the same size, or they were when the movement left the factory, but at some time since then a new screw may have been fitted, perhaps with a slightly different thread. So save time and annoyance when re-assembling ; keep the screws and the parts together.

The date wheel lifts off the cannon pinion. This leaves three jumpers and their springs and three levers and springs for manually stepping the calendar work forward. These pieces can now be removed. It is well to place them on the board paper in their respective positions. Make a mark on the board paper to indicate the position of the winding shaft so that your bench will look something like the illustration (Fig. 149).

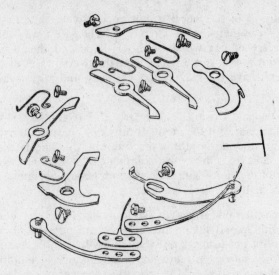

Fig. 149.—*Lay out the parts systematically. Note : Mark on right is to indicate position of the pendant.*

It is now possible to unscrew the wheel gearing into the wheel fitted on to the cannon pinion. This wheel drives the moon and day of the week dials and also the date hand. The months of the year dial is not automatic ; it is stepped forward each month. It is not necessary to remove the steel plate, with spring, and pin, from the wheel *A* (Fig. 150).

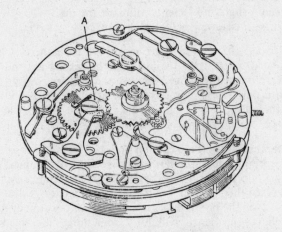

Fig. 150.—*Under the calendar dials.*

The rest of the movement can be taken to pieces and cleaned in the conventional manner. It is better not to place all the calendar parts in the basket of a cleaning machine, but to clean them separately in benzine and replace them in the respective position on the board paper again. There will then be no difficulty in sorting out springs and screws and much time will be saved.

These remarks apply equally to all complicated work. The student must be systematic, methodical, unhurried and careful. It is a good plan to finish the job—at least the complicated part—the same day it is started. If the parts are left on the bench overnight there is the risk of them being disturbed, with consequent loss of time when re-assembling.

Re-Assembling and Oiling

Having assembled the movement, including the keyless and motion work and oiled the pivot holes which will be covered by the calendar mechanism, proceed to assemble the calendar work. First apply a little watch oil to the post on to which the wheel A (Fig. 150) is fitted and screw that wheel into position. Make sure the wheel is perfectly free. Next replace all the jumpers, springs, and levers into position ; apply a little clock oil to the shoulders of the shoulder screws and also a little to the springs where they contact the jumpers, etc. Soak the end of a piece of pegwood, cut chisel-shaped, in clock oil and wipe each of the star teeth of the days of the week and the months of the year dials to grease them. Apply a very little clock oil to the nose of each of the jumpers. This method makes certain that the dials will rotate smoothly. Apply a little watch oil to the posts of these dials and place them in position. Hold the jumpers back with a pointer so that the dials fit on to their posts correctly. Screw down and test each dial to see that it revolves correctly. For this purpose a notch, that can be seen in Fig. 151 is cut into the periphery of the dials so that a pointer can be used to rotate the dial without damaging the surface.

Use watch oil to oil the post for the moon dial and apply a little clock oil to the outside of the pipe of the dial where the tension spring bears upon it. This dial has no jumper. Hold the tension spring back so that the dial seats correctly. Finally replace the date wheel, with no oil to the pipe of the cannon pinion on to which it fits. The dial can now be replaced and then the hands.

First replace the winding shaft and pull out to the hands-set position. Cause the calendar wheel A (Fig. 150) to rotate and observe closely when the day of the week dial jumps. When the jump is completed, place the date hand in position pointing exactly to a figure and then

115

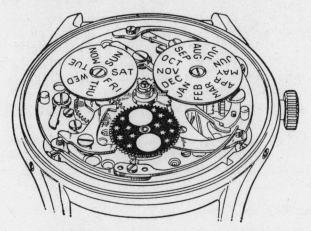

Fig. 151.—*Notches in dials for manual rotation.*

replace the hour hand pointing to 12 o'clock and then the minute hand pointing to the hour. Cause the hands to rotate 24 hours and observe that the date hand and the day of the week dial jump forward as near to 12 (midnight) as possible. The actual movement of the calendar may take half an hour to complete and it is better for the major part of the movement to take place after 12 o'clock.

After replacing the seconds hand, the movement can be fitted into its case and the job is completed. When setting the hands to time, make sure that they are so set that the change of the calendar takes place at midnight, as explained previously. To set the calendar to the correct day and date, the push-pieces at the side of the case are jumped in and out with a pin until the correct reading appears. The moon dial is set by observing the almanack. The calendar dials should not be moved manually while the automatic change is in operation, i.e., between 11.30 p.m. and 12.30 a.m. The most accurate method is to count the age of the moon in days from the new moon. Say the almanack gives the age of the moon on a particular day as 20.2 days ; first step the moon dial to " no moon " and then step it forward 20 plunges which will be as near as it can be set. This method is more accurate than gauging the size of the moon from data given in some diaries.

The function of this calendar watch has not been described in detail because no good purpose would be served. During dismantling as described, the function should be appreciated. It is, as has been observed before, a counting machine, not dissimilar to a speedometer.

When repairing complicated work it is essential to study its action, to be well acquainted with what you are doing, to find out and know *why* certain things happen and what makes them happen. As an instance, look at the pin fitted to the spring piece of the wheel *A* (Fig. 150). Why is the spring used ? Could not the pin be fitted to the wheel as is the other pin which operates the day of the week dial ? If this pin were a fixture, the moon dial would be stepped forward when the hands of the watch were turned backwards. As it is, the spring allows the pin to pass the moon shifting lever without moving the moon dial when the hands are turned backwards ; it can only move the dial forward.

Do not be content to just replace as you find it ; *know why*. Some day you may come across a watch where a previous repairer has lost a part and replaced it with a piece which is not wholly correct, or a part may be replaced upside-down. It happens simply because the man did not understand what he was doing ; he had not made a study of watches. All this may sound naive, but it is very important. To be a good repairer of watches, particularly complicated watches, a man must be a good mechanic and to be a good mechanic he must understand fundamentals. He must study the actual work in hand and do not be satisfied until he knows *WHY*. The designers of watches, especially the mass-produced watches, know why a certain piece has been so designed, and if at first sight it is not obvious to you, think hard and find out. There *is* a good reason and when you have been able to find out what it is, you are well on the way to being a good repairer of complicated work.

Perpetual Calendar

In the perpetual calendar wrist watch (Fig. 152) made by Patek Philippe & Co. of Geneva, Switzerland, the calendar mechanism is fitted to a separate plate which is screwed on to the movement, under the dial. The calendar mechanism can be, and is, used on a chronograph movement as well.

The quality of the work is of an exceptionally high standard. The steel work is finished with a flat fine straight grain with the edges bevelled and polished.

Fig. 152.—*The Patek Philippe perpetual calendar watch.*

117

The action of the calendar mechanism is as follows :—

Fitted on to the hour wheel is the wheel A (Fig. 153). This wheel gears into the intermediate wheel B which in turn gears into the wheel C. Fixed to the wheel C is the pin D and as this wheel rotates in the direction of the arrow it contacts the finger piece E, which is free to rotate on the arbor of the wheel C. Eventually the finger piece E contacts the lever F, which is pivoted at G, and moves it towards the centre of the movement. In doing so, the end of the lever F, at H. steps forward the star wheel I one tooth. This star wheel is controlled by the jumper J. The days of the week dial is screwed on to this star wheel.

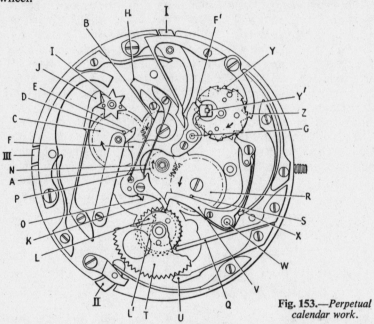

Fig. 153.—*Perpetual calendar work.*

At one end of the lever F the click K is pivoted with a shouldered screw and is kept in contact with the snail M fixed to the star wheel L of 31 teeth by the spring N. As the lever F moves towards the centre, the click O, which is pivoted on to the underside of lever F by a shoulder screw and is controlled by the spring P, steps forward the wheel L one tooth each day. This wheel is controlled by the jumper Q. The elongated pipe of the wheel L carries the hand which indicates the date. The wheel A also gears into the wheel R and the pin S moves forward the star wheel T of 59 teeth, one tooth each day. This wheel is controlled by the jumper U. On the wheel T is painted the phases of the moon dial. The lever V pivoted at W and controlled by the spring X

operates the month star wheel Y which is controlled by the jumper and spring Z. The left-hand end of the lever V is kept in contact on the snail L^1 of the wheel L and upon a complete revolution of this wheel the lever drops down to the smaller radius of the snail. This action moves forward the wheel Y one tooth. Fixed to the wheel Y is a cam with scallops on its edge (*see also* Fig. 154), the full circumference of the cam representing the 31-day months and the scallops the 30-day months.

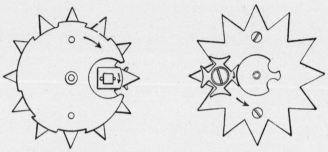

Fig. 154.—*The Leap Year mechanism from front and back.*

The nose of the lever F, at F^1 rests upon the edge of the cam fitted to the wheel Y and it is the depth that the lever F is allowed to move which controls the movement of the wheel L when there are less than 31 days in the month. The snail M, which is fitted above the snail L^1 has a lesser drop than the snail which operates the cam Y. The click K operates on the edge of this snail. If there are 30 days then the click F will be drawn back so that it will move the wheel L two teeth, one in addition to movement given by the click O ; if there are 28 days then the click K will be drawn back to pick up the step in the snail M four days earlier and move the wheel forward four teeth.

The 28 days of February are accommodated by means of the rectangular block Y^1. Three sides of this block are equidistant from the centre and when the nose of the lever F at F' rests upon one of these sides it allows the click K to pick up the step in the snail four days earlier and so move the date wheel forward from the 28th of February to the 1st of March.

Leap Year Mechanism

For leap year the side of the block furthermost from the centre is presented. The lever F cannot drop so far and the click K therefore picks up the step three days earlier and moves the date wheel from the 29th of February to the 1st of March. The block Y^1, is squared on to the star wheel of the Maltese stopwork-like mechanism (Fig. 154).

119

The finger piece remains stationary and as the wheel *Y* rotates once in 12 months so the star wheel of the Maltese Cross wheel rotates once in four years.

An ingenious device is employed so that if the hands are set backwards the calendar work is not deranged. The cock of the wheel *C* is of spring steel and as the wheel *C* is made to rotate in the opposite direction to the arrow, the pin *D* will push the cock up slightly as it passes under the finger piece *E*, the back edge being chamfered to facilitate this. The finger piece *E* is free to rotate on to the arbor of the wheel *C* as already mentioned.

If for some reason the watch has been allowed to run down it will be necessary to consider the calendar work. With a perpetual calendar some care must be taken. If the calendar is only one day out then the best method is to set the hands forward 24 hours, taking care to see that the change-over of the date, etc., is at midnight, as already explained when dealing with the simple calendar watch previously.

When it is necessary to set the calendar after a lapse of several days or months, the push pieces set into the side of the case should be employed. They are pushed inwards with the point of a pin.

The push piece *I* (Fig. 143) actuates the main lever *F* and the whole of the calendar work is moved forward, just as the watch will do when it is wound. If the push piece is depressed to its full extent and then released it is equivalent to 24 hours running of the watch. If it is found necessary to step the phase of the moon only, the piece *II* is depressed ; this will not interfere with other parts of the calendar work. To set the moon dial correctly refer to page 116.

To change the day of the week dial only the push *III* is depressed ; here again the rest of the calendar work is not affected.

It should be noted that the push pieces must not be used at the time of day when they would ordinarily be moved automatically during the running of the watch, say between 6.30 p.m. and 12.30 a.m.

Patek Philippe recommend the procedure as follows when re-assembling the movement after repair :—

Assemble the movement up to but not including the calendar work or the plate on to which it is fitted.

Fit the movement into its case with the three push pieces in position in the case and the winding button and shaft.

Then screw the plate into position, and on to this plate fit the three intermediate wheels, 10, 17 and 24, with their screws (Fig. 155).

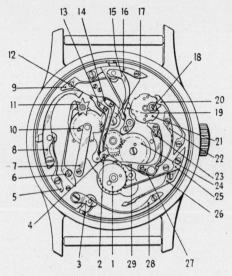

Fig. 155.—*Assembly chart.*

Fit the wheel 1 with its jumper 25.

Fit the lever 29 with its click 23 and the springs 22 and 27.

Next fit the Maltese Cross piece with its rectangular block 18 pinned together, and the months cam 21 on to the twelve-star wheel. After this has been assembled, place it on its stud and then fit the jumper 20.

Now fix the manual setting levers, 3, 8 and 15 with their springs, 28, 5 and 9.

Fit the day of the week star wheel 11 and its jumper 6, then the cock 7, which holds down the finger piece 10.

Assemble on to the lever 12 the clicks 2 and 4 with their respective springs 13 and 14, and the nose 19.

Place the assembled lever 12 in position with the spring 16.

Fit the moon jumper 26.

Important Note.—The parts 2, 4, 18, 23 and their shoulder screws are not oiled, they are left perfectly dry. All other parts where friction occurs are carefully and sparingly oiled with clock oil.

Setting the Date

To set the date, advance the wheel 1 until it makes the lever 29 drop on to the small radius of the snail. Then withdraw the winding button and cause the mechanism to move, in a clockwise direction, until the lever 12 releases the nose 19 from the wheel 21. The lever 29 is then operated manually so to bring the rectangular block 18 facing the nose 19. When the face of the block which is furthest from the centre is facing the nose 19, it is in the position of February in Leap Year. To set this month cam to the correct month, the cam is moved by operating the lever 29, each movement equals one month. If, for instance, the month is August of the second year after Leap Year, the lever 29 is operated manually 32 times. The moon intermediate wheel 24 must have its pin on the line of centres of the wheel 24 and the lever 29, when this lever drops on to the smaller radius of the snail, i.e., at midnight.

Now fit the dial discs on to their respective wheels, making sure that the months cam 21 does not move while this is being done.

Replace the dial of the watch and fit the hands pointing to 12 o'clock immediately the day of the week disc has jumped after setting the handwork forward ; the hands are now indicating midnight.

The date hand is fitted pointing to the first day.

The moon dial is set manually by the push piece *II* (Fig. 153), and for instructions how to set correctly refer to page 116.

The day of the week is set manually by the push piece *III*.

Should it be found necessary to remove the fully assembled movement from its case, make quite sure that the push pieces *I*, *II* and *III* are well back in the middle band of the case before refitting the movement into its case again, so as to avoid damage to the balance or the setting levers.

There are many methods employed to achieve the same object in perpetual calendar watches, but the broad fundamental principle is the same. No good purpose would be served to describe them all, even if that were possible.

Study the mechanism well before dismantling to know exactly what happens, and why.

Section 7

REPEATERS AND CLOCK WATCHES

The term repeaters refers to watches (and clocks) which can be made to repeat the time at will, and such watches strike the hours, quarters, and, in some watches, the minutes which have just passed.

It has been constantly stressed that the utmost care must be exercised when repairing complicated watches, and when repairing repeating watches, that advice can now be doubly stressed.

We have all heard the phrase *cool, calm and collected*, and it can be applied to meet many occasions, but it has a real personal significance to the person undertaking the repair of repeaters.

Cool ; To be confident and assured that the necessary skill has been acquired to undertake such work, in other words, to be a proficient craftsman.

Calm ; To be quiet and peaceful, not to be in an agitated frame of mind. To be possessed of great patience and some determination and certainly not to be in a hurry or to be flurried.

Collected ; To have your wits about you, to be alert and with an ordered mind, to be systematic and precise.

This may sound formidable, but we all possess these qualities in varying degrees and it is for the student to make himself proficient, by acquiring through practice, the mentality *necessary* to do the work now to be discussed.

First and foremost is to be a good craftsman through constant practice at repairing non-complicated watches and then to automatic winding watches and then chronographs. It is essential to be able to fathom things out—to find out why. This statement has often been repeated, one *must* know how it works and it will be the aim when dealing with repeaters to explain in the fullest detail each working part, so that if the craftsman were presented with a box containing a repeating watch movement, dismantled and in disorder, he would be able to re-assemble it, build it up, piece by piece, knowing what was required of each part.

Types of Repeater

Types of repeating watches can be divided under five headings :—

Quarter Repeaters : Repeating the hours and quarters.

123

Half Quarter Repeaters : Repeating the hours, quarters, and also the half quarters, by a single note on the high-pitched gong after 7½ minutes past the hour. At 20 minutes to 3 o'clock, for example, the watch will strike 2 hours, 2 quarters and 1 blow to indicate that it is after 7½ minutes past the half hour.

Five Minute Repeaters : Repeating the hours and then 1 blow on a high pitched gong for each 5 minutes past the hour. At say, 4 minutes to 3 o'clock, 2 blows for the hours and then 11 blows will be struck to indicate 55 minutes, at least, past the last hour : it will indicate to the nearest five minutes.

Minute Repeaters : Repeating the hours, quarters, and then the minutes on a high pitched gong. At 3 hours 59 minutes for instance —2 blows for the hours, 3 ting-tangs for the three-quarters and then 14 blows to indicate 14 minutes past the three-quarters.

Clock Watches : Such watches are minute repeaters and in addition they strike the hours and quarters in passing, as does a striking clock. These watches are provided with a mainspring for the strike—and repeating—train which is wound daily. When required to repeat, a release piece is operated. It is not necessary to wind the spring each time as in the case of ordinary repeating watch.

They will be dealt with in that order.

Quarter Repeaters

Quarter repeaters strike, at will, the last hour and then the last quarter, or quarters, of an hour.

The hours are struck on a deep-toned gong and the quarters by a ting-tang, first a blow on the deep-toned gong and then a blow on a higher pitched toned gong, in quick succession. At say, 5 minutes to 9 o'clock, 8 blows on the deep-toned gong and then 3 ting-tangs will indicate the time to the nearest quarter of an hour.

Fig. 157 illustrates the simplest form of quarter repeater made. In order that the instructions shall be as explicit as possible, the movement will be taken to pieces and re-assembled, part by part. Then repairs will be discussed. Oiling will be dealt with as we proceed with the assembly.

The beginner with quarter repeaters is advised to read the whole of the assembly instructions before attempting to dismantle, and then to start taking the watch to pieces when fully acquainted with the working of the parts. It is felt that this method is less confusing than to describe dismantling. Wind up the repeating train a little by drawing round the slide. Then block the train by setting the speed control deeper or by placing a chip of pegwood between the repeating escape wheel and the pallets. This takes the tension off the winding and quarter racks, which may then be easily removed. Release the train, let it run down, and then remove the other parts.

First assemble the going train of the watch complete including the repeating train, i.e. the barrel arbor with the wheel working upon it, the two wheels of the train which are pivoted between the plates and also the two hammers.

The mainspring is contained in a barrel screwed to the underside of the upper plate. (Fig. 158). It is important to see that the inner end of the spring is well curved inwards to ensure correct hooking on to the barrel arbor. It is most annoying to find after assembly that the mainspring is not properly hooked, so make sure. The barrel arbor operates in the mainwheel with a ratchet and click as shown in Fig. 159. Fit the barrel arbor into the barrel, making sure that the mainspring is securely hooked on to the hook of the barrel arbor. Oil the mainspring before screwing the barrel into position. Fit the two wheels and the hammers into position as in Fig. 159. With the

(Right) **Fig. 156.**—*The simplest form of quarter repeater.*

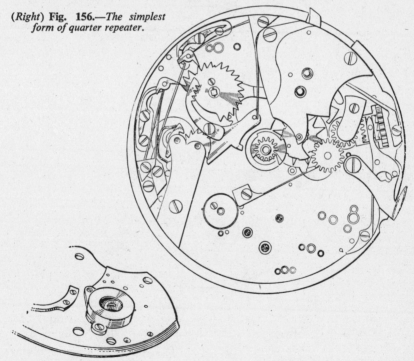

Fig. 157.—*The repeater mainspring barrel.*

barrel arbor hanging from the upper plate, carefully manipulate the pivots into their respective holes and screw the plate down securely.

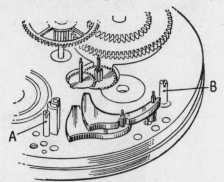

Fig. 158.—*Repeater mainspring barrel and arbor and main wheel.*

Fig. 159.—*The wheels and hammers in position. A—screw for adjusting speed of repeating. B—dial screw.*

We are then left with the plate under the dial as illustrated in Fig. 160.

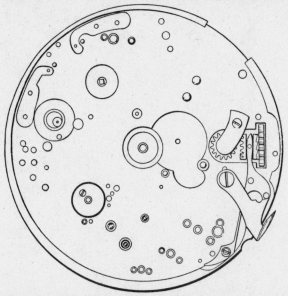

Fig. 160.—*Under the dial before assembly of repeating works.*

Next screw the two hammer banking pieces into position. The screws *A* and *B* (Fig. 161) control the depth of the hammers on to the gongs. The underside of the heads are cone shaped so that as the screws are screwed in further so the hammers are held further away from the gongs. The tone of the gongs should be adjusted by these screws, before the dial is replaced. As the dial can be fitted after the movement has been fitted into its case, this arrangement is quite convenient. Some repeaters are so made that the adjustment can be made from the other side of the movement, with the dial on and while in its case, as we shall see later.

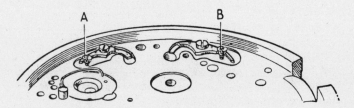

Fig. 161.—*Adjustments for hammer banking pieces.* A *and* B—*screws for adjusting tone of gongs.*

Next fit the repeater escape wheel and pallets into position and screw on the cock holding these parts (Fig. 162). The speed of running of the repeating train is controlled by the wire *A* which is fixed to a plug. The other end of this plug has an extended end with a slot cut into it, screw-like. The speed can therefore be adjusted after the movement has been fully assembled and is in its case. If the slotted end is turned so that the wire is brought closer to the tail of the pallets, the speed of the train is increased. After complete assembly the direction of turning is ascertained by trial ; in this particular movement a clockwise turn makes the train slower because the wire is brought further away from the tail of the pallets and therefore they can engage deeper into the escape wheel.

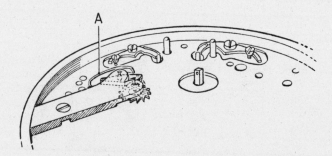

Fig. 162.—*Repeater escape wheel and pallets in position.*

Before placing the pallets into position the lower hole should be oiled. Apply a little watch oil to the lower pivot of the star wheel and place that into position and then the jumper which controls it.

Speed of Repeating

The speed of the repeating is sometimes regulated or controlled by a governor as in Fig. 162. The centre arm is fixed to the last pinion of the train and the two pivoted weights are mounted on the arm where they are controlled by two light springs. As the governor rotates, the arms open out by centifrugal force. The speed depends upon the weight of the weights and the strength of their springs. There is not much scope to control the speed other than to manipulate the springs. If the speed is too slow the springs should be bent inwards to increase the resistance. The arms will then not open out so much and the speed will be increased. Conversely, if the speed is too fast the springs should be bent so that they bear more lightly upon the arms of the weights and they will open out more. Should the springs be made as light as possible and the speed still be too great, there is little that can be done about it other than to make the weights a little heavier. This presents a problem but fortunately one is rarely faced with this difficulty.

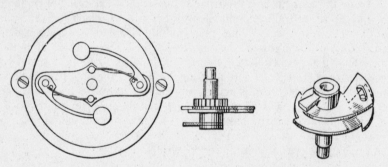

Fig. 163.—*Repeating governor.*   Fig. 164.—*Cannon pinion, showing snail and surprise piece.*

In another system of controlling the speed the last pinion of the train has fitted to its arbor a brass collet and the upper pivot works in a hole drilled through a plug off centre, so that the pivot hole is eccentric. The plug has a slot cut across its centre—screw-like—so that if the plug is turned with a screwdriver, depth of engagement of the pinion with the wheel it gears into can be altered. If the depth is made shallow the speed is quickened and if deep, it is slower.

The cannon pinion has fitted to it a snail of four steps which control the number of quarters to be struck. On its underside is the surprise piece (Fig. 164). The purpose of this is to ensure that the rack, which falls upon it, cannot drop during the 15 minutes past the hour when no quarters are required. As the centre wheel rotates, it carries with it the cannon pinion and the tail of the surprise piece makes contact with the star wheel (Fig. 165) and moves it one tooth. As it jumps under the influence of the jumper spring, it flicks forward the surprise piece to the position as shown in Fig. 166.

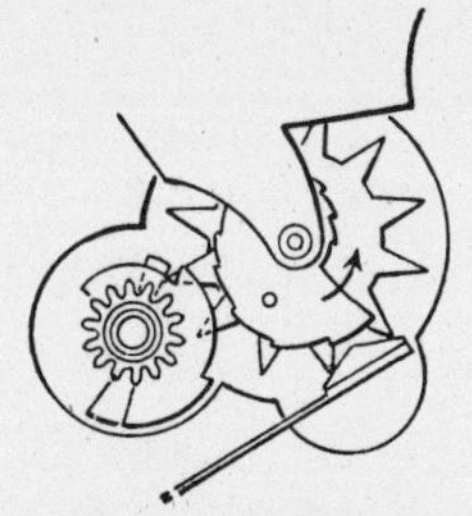

Fig. 165.—*Surprise piece makes contact with star wheel which shuts back surprise piece.*

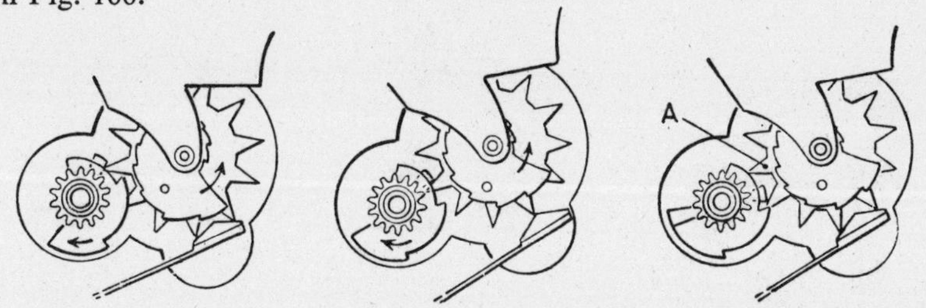

Fig. 166.—*Surprise piece flicked forward into position, shown in three stages.*

As the cannon pinion rotates, the star wheel tooth it will contact next moves the surprise piece back to its normal position so that the tail of the quarter rack can drop on to the lowest step and allow three quarters to be struck. The surprise piece must be perfectly free with no perceptible up and down shake. If it is at all tight it will not flick forward, and also it will move the star wheel a quarter of an hour before its time. After the cannon has been cleaned (it is not always necessary to remove the surprise piece) make quite sure it is *perfectly* dry and blow it out well with the bellows to ensure that there is no dust between the surprise piece and cannon pinion. Move the surprise piece backward and forward many times and well blow with the bellows —*never* with the mouth—while it is in different positions. The surprise piece *must not* be oiled ; the slightest amount of oil, however thin, would cause it to drag.

Apply a little clock oil to the arbor of the centre wheel and snap the cannon pinion into position ; make sure that tongue of the surprise piece is free of the star wheel teeth, otherwise, when snapping on, the tongue may damage a tooth.

Next oil, with clock oil, the pivot of the barrel arbor and place the small steel wheel with the square hole on to the square of the barrel arbor. With a long watch key wind up the repeating mainspring to its full extent (Fig. 167). The long handle to the key is almost essential, as it is more convenient than, say, the pin tongs, as the watchmaker can then see what he is doing. If you have no such keys it is well worth while making one or two up. They are quite simple to make ; use the pipe from an ordinary watch key and solder or pin it into the end of a piece of brass rod about 3 inches long, the diameter being a little larger than the diameter of the key pipe. A reminder here ; make sure that all the pivot holes of the going train are oiled. It is too late to do this when the repeating work has been assembled.

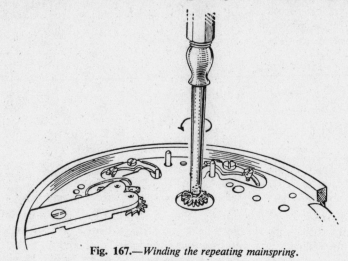

Fig. 167.—*Winding the repeating mainspring.*

Setting up the Repeating Mainspring

When the mainspring is fully wound, allow the train to run down one turn of the barrel arbor and hold up the train. Then place the winding rack into position so that the teeth engage as in Fig. 168.

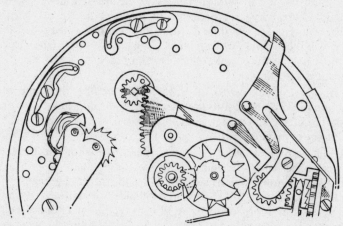

Fig. 168.—*Position of winding rack teeth with relation to repeating pinion when mainspring is " set up " but not wound.*

130

Release the mainspring again and the train will run until it is arrested by the rack contacting the block, as Fig. 169. In this manner the mainspring is " set up," so that when the long hours are struck—say at 12.45—there will not be a slackening of speed through want of power. If when the barrel arbor has unwound one turn, the position of the small steel wheel, or pinion, is not correct, allow the train to run down a little further. Should it be necessary to let it run further in order to bring the wheel into the correct position for proper engagement with the winding rack, then stop the train by holding the pallets with a piece of peg wood, remove the winding wheel and replace it on another square where required. (Sometimes the square is marked to indicate the appropriate position for the wheel.) One must ensure that when the repeating mainspring is wound, say to repeat at 12.45, there is still at least one turn left before pulling on the hook.

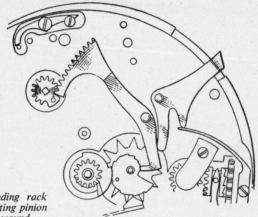

Fig. 169.—*Position of winding rack teeth with relation to repeating pinion when mainspring is fully wound.*

In some of the better quality movements the barrel is provided with a ratchet wheel and click—usually click and spring combined—the purpose of which is to set the mainspring up when the racks are assembled. Even so, it is more satisfactory to set the spring up as explained.

Next place the slide which operates the winding rack in position and oil the studs on to which both these pieces fit with a little clock oil. Now screw on the cock holding these two pieces down and also the upper support of the star wheel.

It is always advisable to fit the movement into its case as early as possible during assembly, and the time has now arrived when this movement can be cased up. The watchmaker is then better able to handle the movement and wind up the repeating train by drawing round the slide.

Now screw the hour rack on to the mainspring winding pinion and then place on its stud the rack which determines the number of quarters to be struck, together with its spring. A pin is fitted to the tail of the quarter rack so that when the rack is gathered up at the completion of striking it contacts the escape wheel of the repeating train and so

131

stops it. The movement now appears as in Fig. 170. In this illustration the cock over the star wheel and the winding rack has been left off, but it can be seen in position in Fig. 156, the complete movement.

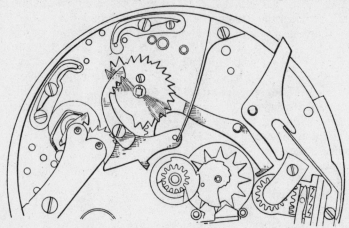

Fig. 170.—*Movement with hour rack and quarter rack in position.*

It now only remains to fit the hammer pallets into position. Apply a little watch oil to the pivot holes of each of the hammers and what oil is left on the oiler smear on to the extended pivots of the hammers. It is on to these pivots that the hammer pallets fit. The springs operating the pallets are light and to over-oil would be dangerous. Before placing the pallets into position, fit the two hammer springs and apply a very little clock oil to the point where the springs make contact. Apply very little watch oil to the ends of the fine pallet return springs where they enter the holes in the pallets. When fitting some springs, the quarter rack spring for instance, it is better partially to screw home the spring and then lift the end up and lead it into its correct position and finally screw home. Some craftsmen screw the springs firmly into position first and then guide them into position afterwards. This practice can be dangerous as in some instances it places too great a strain on the spring, which may break. Apply a little clock oil to the quarter rack spring, smear the two faces of the star wheel jumper spring, and also the faces of the two hammer pallets, with clock oil. Apply a little watch oil to the lever fitted on to the quarter rack and also to the pivots of the pallets, escape wheel and the star wheel.

We can now screw the gongs into position. Make sure they are fixed very firmly ; loose gongs make for bad tone. Now test the repeating for speed and tone ; the methods of adjustment have already been explained.

Action of the Quarter Repeater

The action of the quarter repeater is as follows :—

The slide A (Fig. 171) is drawn round and this eventually winds up the repeating mainspring as much as is required. The hour rack B is thus made to rotate anti-clockwise and in so doing the two hammer pallets C and D are deflected to one side. The teeth (1 to 12 on the hour rack B) that are allowed to pass the hammer pallets lift the hammer on their return and cause the blows to be struck. The number of blows is determined by the snail E, and if the tail of the winding rack contacts the snail so as to allow 7 teeth to pass, 7 blows will be struck. The pallet C contacts the hammer pin F and upon its release the blows are struck under the impetus of the spring G.

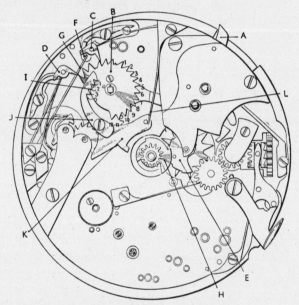

Fig. 171.—*Quarter repeating movement.*

The quarters are controlled by the snail H. When the slide is drawn at, say, after half past an hour (as illustrated in Fig. 171). the pin I, fixed to the rack B, releases the claw-like lever J, which is pivoted on to the quarter rack K, and under the influence of the spring L the rack drops on to the snail H. When the hours have finished striking the 4-toothed claw arrests the hour rack so that two ting-tangs only are sounded by the two sets of three teeth on the hour rack. If the claw were not there, the hour rack would continue to rotate and three ting-tangs would be sounded each time the slide was drawn. The illustration shows that two teeth have been gathered up and therefore two ting-tangs are sounded. At any time from the hour to quarter past, the quarter rack drops just sufficiently to allow the pin on the rack K to free the escape wheel, and when the hours have finished striking the pin I will contact the tooth O on the claw and the hour rack will draw it up and so stop the train, and no quarters will be struck.

To continue the assembly, place the minute and hour wheels in position and fit the dial. Set the hand work clockwise, slowly, and listen carefully until you hear the star wheel jump. Draw the slide and count the number of blows and then fit the hour hand to correspond. At the same time fit on the minute hand lightly. Now set the hands forward again until the minute hand reaches, say, 1 to $\frac{1}{2}$ a minute to the hour, and let the going train carry the hands. Listen again and at the precise moment the star wheel jumps observe the minute hand. If it points dead on the hour minute mark, press the hand firmly into position : if not, move the hand slightly to its supposedly correct position and set the hands round one hour again, continuing thus until it is correct, and then—and not until—press the hand firmly on. Try the hands round at each quarter, set to, say, $\frac{1}{4}$ minute to the quarter hour, and let the watch carry the hand to the exact quarter hour and then try the repeating ; it should not strike the quarter until the quarter hour has been reached. Repeat this test at the $\frac{1}{2}$ hour and $\frac{1}{4}$ to the hour. When setting the hands manually a slight strain is imposed on the centre arbor so that the position of the minute hand may not be true when you hear the star wheel jump. It is, therefore, advisable to let the train operate the star wheel in a " natural " way ; all strains and minor faults, etc., are then accounted for.

Better Quality Quarter Repeaters

Fig. 172 is of a better quality quarter repeater. The fundamental principle is the same as Fig. 171. The winding pinion is on the top of the winding rack and the quarter rack is gathered up by the hook-shaped piece squared on to the barrel arbor.

With the movement in Fig. 173 the number of hours to be struck depends, to a great extent, upon the amount the slide is drawn round. By drawing the slide partially, i.e. not to the full extent so that the tail reaches to the step on the snail, any number of hours—less than the correct number—can be struck.

In the movement Fig. 172 there is a refinement the " all-or-nothing " piece A, which controls the striking so that the full number of hours are struck, or nothing at all. This operates in the following manner : The winding rack has the rack tail pivoted on to it by a shouldered screw (Fig. 173), i.e. the part that contacts the hour snail. It is not solid with the rack as that in Fig. 171. Also pivoted on to the rack

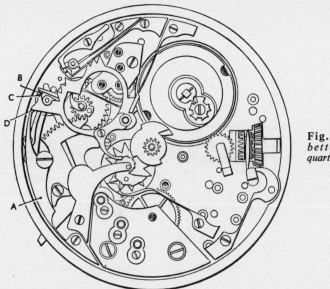

Fig. 172.—*A better quality quarter repeater.*

(Fig. 173) by a shouldered screw is the small lever *B*. When the slide is drawn round to wind the repeating train, the tongue *C* contacts the lever, and only when the rack tail is pressed hard on to the snail does the other end of the small lever contact the all-or-nothing piece *D*. This piece is a spring and the extra pressure on the slide will move it to one side and allow the rack to fall and free the hour hammer pallet (Fig. 174).

Fig. 173.—*Operation of all-or-nothing piece.*

Fig. 174.—*Hour hammer pallet free.*

135

The hour hammer pallet of the better quality quarter repeater is separate from the quarter pallet and has fitted to it a long pin B (Fig. 172). When the quarter rack is gathered up the end of the rack, C, contacts this pin and holds it to one side out of the path of the hour rack. The end of the all-or-nothing piece has a step cut into it, and when the rack is gathered up fully the all-or-nothing piece springs down, so locking the rack, and at the same time the hour pallet is held out of the path of the hour rack. Therefore, no hours or quarters can be struck until the slide is drawn round decisively.

Upon completion of striking, the repeating train is arrested by the hook on the barrel arbor contacting the quarter rack and binding it against the hour hammer post ; the block on the winding pinion takes some of the strain also.

When assembling repeaters with all-or-nothing piece mechanism it is necessary to wind the repeating train partly by drawing the slide and holding it thus while the quarter rack is being placed in position. It will be appreciated, especially in this instance, that it is always advisable to get the movement into its case as soon as possible as it is much more convenient to handle.

Repairs

As with most watch work, repairs would be simple if it were not for the other man. The necessity for the majority of repairs in complicated work is due to maltreatment by some previous person. The repairs due to wear are straightforward and in the case of repeating watches are usually the polishing of pivots and rebushing holes.

The replacement of broken springs, levers, etc., means making them by hand, since they are not, as a rule, interchangeable. The number of repeating watches in circulation is, by comparison with other watches, very, small and material dealers do not stock spare parts. In a great many instances it is practically impossible to find the manufacturers.

What faults is the repeater heir to ? They are few if the watch is left alone, but alas, in practice, they are many and the majority are due to filing to reduce something. A golden rule is *to think well before you act*. Sometimes it is found that a rack tail has been interfered with, perhaps to correct a faulty number of hours being struck. Before reducing, make sure the fault is not in the rack. The pivot holes of the star wheel may be a little large, in which case rebush to make sure. See that the snail is screwed tightly on to the star wheel and that the rack stud is firm. Having assured yourself upon these points, try the repeating again. If the fault is a stubborn one

136

it is advisable to get a second opinion. This may not always be possible and in such circumstances it is a good plan to give the job a rest and come back to it fresh say in an hour or two. Always bear in mind that it must have been right originally. A time may come when something must be done. Do it by degrees : correcting one fault may create another.

If you find that the part has been filed, then the remedy is comparatively simple. Start from the beginning, by removing the results of wear first, that is, " fair wear and tear," such as enlarged pivot holes, both of the star wheel and the hammers. When this is done, try the repeating. If an excess of blows is registered it may be found that the tail of the winding rack has been stretched. That being so, move the star wheel round and try all the hours. At 1 o'clock 2 blows are struck, for instance, and an additional blow at the other 11 hours. The remedy then is to reduce the end of the rack tail until the correct number of blows is struck. But if the number of blows is irregular,

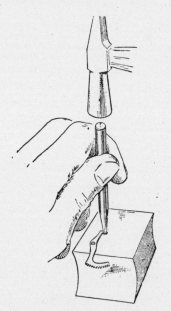

i.e. 2 at 1 o'clock, 3 at 2 o'clock, but 4 o'clock is correct, then this is more difficult. First examine the steps of the snail and see if they have been tampered with. If, say, one of the steps has been reduced, the remedy is simple, but tedious to rectify. First reduce the other 10 steps so that each hour is one in excess, in other words that all the steps decrease by an amount equal to one blow. Then stretch the tail to correct for the one blow which is in excess on all the steps.

To stretch the tail, first test for temper ; if very hard let the extreme tip of the tail down to a deep blue. Then place upside down on a hardened polished steel stake and with a rounded-end, chisel-shaped punch give a smart blow with a fairly heavy hammer—say a clock hammer—near the end of the tail, to spread it (*see* Fig. 175).

Fig. 175.—*Stretching the tail of the winding rack.*

As there is no means of controlling the amount of the stretching, it may be necessary to give further treatment. On the other hand, it may be necessary to reduce by stoning the end of the tip with an Arkansas slip. Testing in the watch is the only means of finding out.

To reduce the steps of the snail, first remove it from the star wheel and then use an iron polisher charged with oilstone dust and oil. In this manner the same curves and sharpness of the angles can be maintained and also the risk of reducing too much is minimised, the process of reducing is slow.

After all alterations finish the surfaces as they were originally. *See* " Practical Watch Repairing." pages 163-177. Sometimes it is found that the last hammer blow of the quarters fails to drop because the rack has gathered up the pallet and has not been lifted far enough. This is generally due to the hammer hole being worn and needing rebushing, or the post of the hammer on to which the pallet is fitted being bent. To straighten the post do so in much the same manner as a train pivot is straightened with hot, smooth-jawed, flat-nose pliers.

Sometimes the wearer of a repeater complains that the quarters strike too soon after the hours, not giving sufficient time for the hours to be counted. The fault may be, in the instance of the system as Fig. 171, that the pin in the hour rack is loose or that it is bent. If it is found to be quite tight and upright, then bend it slightly away from the claw-like rack so that the quarter rack is not gathered up so quickly.

With the system as Fig. 172, the quarter rack gathering hook may not be on its correct square, or the square hole in the hook is large. This being so, close it with a round-end punch from the under side ; place on the hard steel stake—upside down—and with the hammer give the punch two or three medium blows. If you are satisfied that the matters referred to are in order, then reduce the end of the hook slightly so to delay the quarter rack being gathered up.

These one or two repairs have been explained more to indicate the *approach* to correcting faults rather than to lay down hard and fast rules of actual repairs.

The *first* general rule is to rectify wear.

Second is to detect maltreatment by others.

Third is to reason why the maltreatment was carried out. This gives the clue to its correction.

Fourth is to think well before you act ; it is easy to take off, or reduce, but it is not so simple to add or make up.

Fifth is to make sure that one fault corrected is not at the expense of another. The more complicated the watch the more easily this can be done.

Half-Quarter Repeater

Half-quarter repeaters (Fig. 176) are rarely met with now. The hours and quarters are struck in the normal manner and in addition one blow is struck after the hour or the quarters, i.e. after $7\frac{1}{2}$ minutes past the hour, the $\frac{1}{4}$, $\frac{1}{2}$ hour or $\frac{1}{4}$ to the hour. At, say, 10 minutes to 2 o'clock, one blow for the hour, 3 ting-tangs for the $\frac{1}{4}$ to the hour, and then one blow on the low-toned gong. At after $7\frac{1}{2}$ minutes past the hour, one blow is struck after the previous hour was struck.

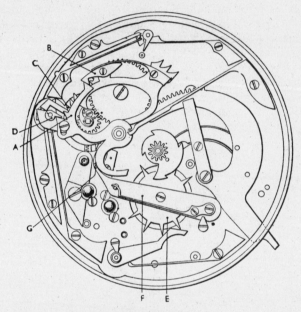

Fig. 176.—*The half-quarter repeater.*

The mechanism is practically the same as the quarter repeater. Superimposed on the quarter rack is a small rack of one tooth A (Fig. 176), and the tail of this rack operates on the snail superimposed on the quarter snail, fixed to the cannon pinion. There are five steps on this snail. The first does not allow the rack to fall sufficiently for the one tooth to pass the hammer pallet. Therefore if the slide is drawn during this period, i.e. up to $7\frac{1}{2}$ minutes past the hour, no $\frac{1}{2}$-$\frac{1}{4}$ will be struck.

The $\frac{1}{2}$-$\frac{1}{4}$ snail (Fig. 177) is positioned so that its steps overlap the $\frac{1}{4}$ snail by half their length so that if the $\frac{1}{4}$ rack falls on to its snail when the $\frac{1}{2}$-$\frac{1}{4}$ rack falls on to the overlapping half, the additional movement of the $\frac{1}{4}$ rack causes the click B (Figs. 176 and 179) to lift and arrest the $\frac{1}{2}$-$\frac{1}{4}$ rack A.

139

Fig. 177.—*The ½-¼ snail.*    **Fig. 178.**—*Additional movement of the snail.*

This small rack cannot then drop, so that its one tooth is exposed in the path of the hammer pallet ; the tooth will coincide with the last tooth *C* of the ¼ rack, therefore no ½-¼ will be struck. But when the ¼ snail has moved half the length of one of its steps, i.e. 7½ minutes, the two snails coincide and one surface is presented to the tails of the two racks (Fig. 178). The one tooth is therefore exposed to the hammer pallet and one blow will be struck. The normal position of the ½-¼ rack is for the one tooth to be exposed and when no ½-¼'s are required the hammer pallet *D* will arrest the ½-¼ rack while the ¼ rack continues to be gathered up. This will lift the click *B* free of the ½-¼ rack. Fig. 179 shows the ½-¼ rack arrested so that no ½-¼ will be struck.

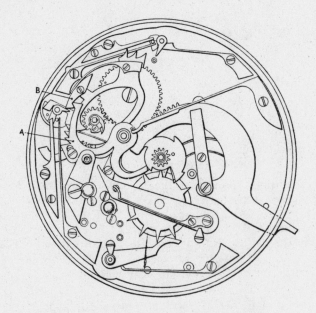

Fig. 179.—*The half-quarter repeater with ½-¼ rack arrested.*

It is interesting to note that the movement illustrated in Figs. 176 and 179 is provided with the older type of " all-or-nothing " mechanism.

The star wheel E, with the hour snail fixed to it, is pivoted to the lever F by a shouldered screw. When the winding rack tail is pressed hard on to the snail it moves the star wheel slightly and this releases the $\frac{1}{4}$ rack, by reason of the end of the lever F being drawn away from the path of the rack at G.

Five-Minute Repeater

The five-minute repeater strikes the hours and then, on a higher-toned gong, one blow for each five minutes ; at say, 7.45, seven blows on the deep-toned gong and then nine blows on the higher-toned gong are struck. Here again this form of repeater is seldom met with and it is difficult to understand why. It is no more complicated than the $\frac{1}{4}$ repeater and less so than either the $\frac{1}{2}$-$\frac{1}{4}$ or minute repeaters.

The snail (Fig. 180) fixed to the cannon pinion has eleven steps so that the maximum of eleven blows can be struck to indicate the time to the nearest five minutes, i.e. a maximum of 55 minutes, 11×5.

The greatest diameter of the snail before the first step will not allow the rack to fall sufficiently for any teeth to pass the hammer pallet, therefore no blows will be struck. The five minute rack is similar to the $\frac{1}{4}$ rack except that instead of two sets of three teeth there are eleven teeth (Fig. 181). When the hours have finished striking the five minute rack is gathered up exactly similarly to the $\frac{1}{4}$ repeater. This system is very simple and strong but it has been sadly neglected by the manufacturers.

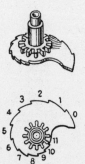
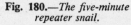

Fig. 180.—*The five-minute repeater snail.*

Fig. 181.—*The five-minute repeater rack* (A).

With both the $\frac{1}{2}$-$\frac{1}{4}$ and the five minute repeaters the same care must be exercised when fitting on the minute hand as has been explained when dealing with the quarter repeater. In the case of the $\frac{1}{2}$-$\frac{1}{4}$, try the minute hand at the quarter, set the hand at, say, half a minute to the hour and then listen for the click of the star wheel jump. Set the hand to half a minute to the quarter past and let the train carry it to the quarter and then draw the repeating slide and it should strike the quarter. Then set the hand to 22 minutes past the hour and when the train has carried it to $22\frac{1}{2}$ minutes draw the slide and it should strike the quarter and one blow for the $\frac{1}{2}$-$\frac{1}{4}$.

The same procedure applies to the five minute repeater, listening first at the hour and then setting to $4\frac{1}{2}$ minutes past and draw the slide at five minutes past, and so on.

If it is found that striking is not *exact* at all the quarters, $\frac{1}{2}$-$\frac{1}{4}$'s or five minutes, as the case may be, then we must compromise and replant the minute hand so that the *least* error is shown at all the points, in other words, divide or spread the error. Should an error exist there are many contributory faults and the greatest may be the positioning of the dial. If the dial has feet it can be moved slightly ; say the hour is correct but at the half hour the striking is a little fast, i.e. it strikes at the half hour at half a minute after it should, pushing the lower half of the dial slightly to the left will correct this and not interfere with the hour. To move the dial safely, hold the handle end of the watch brush against the edge of the dial at a point below the quarter past and give it a light blow with the watch hammer. (Fig. 182). There is, as a rule, just that freedom of the dial feet in their holes to allow the dial to move slightly. Other than this adjustment, it is, generally speaking, not worth going further because the alterations necessary are numerous ; length of the steps of the $\frac{1}{4}$ snail ; centre wheel slightly out of upright ; holes a shade too large, and so on.

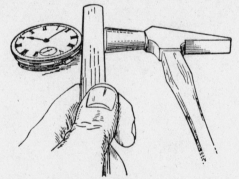

Fig. 182.—*A method of moving the dial with safety.*

Minute Repeater

The minute repeater (Fig. 183) is, perhaps, the more popular of all repeaters. It strikes the hours, quarters and then one blow for each minute past the quarter. At say 3.55 it will strike 3 on the deep-toned gong, three ting-tongs and then 10 single blows on the higher-toned gong.

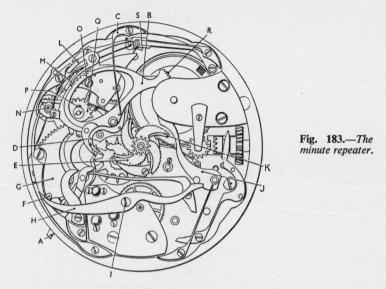

Fig. 183.—*The minute repeater.*

We shall start with the movement assembled up to the ¼ repeater stage as in Fig. 184, which has already been fully described and we shall assume that the movement has been fitted into its case, as advised.

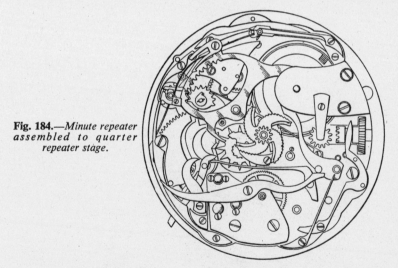

Fig. 184.—*Minute repeater assembled to quarter repeater stage.*

In addition to the ¼ snail the cannon pinion has fitted to it the minute snail which consists of four arms each with 14 steps (Fig. 185). It is also provided with a surprise piece which has four arms and is operated by a flirt and spring. As the cannon pinion rotates clockwise the

143

beak of the flirt contacts the surprise piece and pushes it to one side. (Fig. 186) the cannon continues to rotate and the flirt rides on the top of the surprise piece and as it leaves the flirt springs down and gives the surprise piece a kick which flirts it forward as in Figs. 187-8. The surprise piece has now extended the first part of the snail so that it is not possible for the minute rack to drop down to the last step and so allow 14 minutes to be struck when no minutes at all should be sounded.

Fig. 185.—*The minute snail.*

As the cannon rotates with the surprise piece still drawn out, the flirt will, before the next quarter hour, close the surprise in, so that the long minutes can be struck and, at the proper time, it will flirt it forward again.

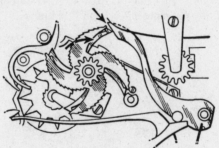

Fig. 186.—*Minute snail about to contact flirt.*

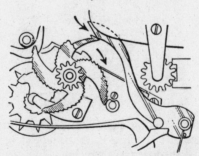

Fig. 187.—*Flirt riding on top of minute surprise piece. (Minute snail cut away)*

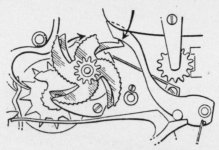

Fig. 188.—*Flirt giving kick to minute surprise piece, thus flirting surprise piece forward.* *(Minute snail cut away).*

The star wheel, to which the hour snail is fixed, is moved forward by the flirt fitted to the quarter snail and, the quarter snail is fixed to the surprise piece therefore as the cannon rotates this flirt contacts a tooth of the star wheel which causes the surprise piece to come forward into action and with it the quarter snail. Thus no quarters can be struck, but the long minutes are free to be struck. Thereafter the flirt takes control of the surprise piece and eventually flirts it forward, as already explained when speaking of the quarters.

When the slide is drawn to repeat, a stop lever is released which allows the flirt to drop deeper and if this happens at the hour or up to one minute past, the flirt bears down on to the surprise piece and holds it firmly in position.

As with the ¼ snail no oil is applied to the minute snail. A very little clock oil is smeared on to the beak of the flirt. It is frequently found that the beak of the flirt is either red with friction rust or coated with a residue of thick oil. The former may be due to over oiling with too thin an oil, where the oil has been drawn away. In the latter case it is because of over oiling with thick oil. The surface should be just greased with a reasonably thick oil, such as clock oil.

Fitted on to the same post as the quarter rack and frequently on to an extended pipe of this rack, is the minute rack *B* (Fig. 183). It will be noted that there are two sets of teeth. The 14 at one end are for the minutes and the other set of six teeth to gather up the minute rack. Pivoted on to the quarter rack by a shouldered screw is the pawl *L* (Fig. 183) which is kept in contact with the rack by a spring. When the slide is drawn round, the ¼ rack drops on to its snail and the limb of the pawl contacts the hammer post which holds it free of the minute rack which drops on to its snail. When the minute rack drops to its lowest step on the snail to strike 14 minutes, the pawl engages in the last space of the six teeth on the rack and so gathers up the rack to allow 14 blows to be struck. When the rack drops to strike up to 4 minutes, the pawl engages the first tooth of the 6 ;

145

5, and 6 blows, the first space ; 7 and 8 blows the second space ; 9 and 10 the third space ; 11 and 12 the fourth space ; finally 13 and 14 the fifth space. If it were not for this pawl the quarter rack could not gather up the minute rack to allow the higher number of minutes to be struck. Fig. 189 shows the pawl held out of action by the hammer post and Fig. 190 the pawl about to gather up the minute rack to strike 7 minutes.

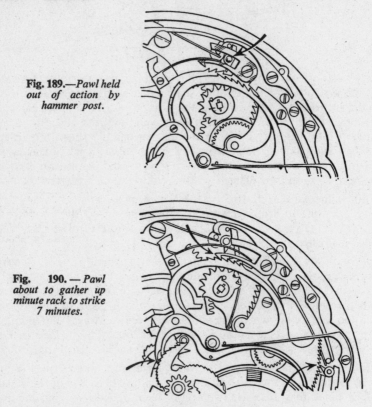

Fig. 189.—*Pawl held out of action by hammer post.*

Fig. 190.—*Pawl about to gather up minute rack to strike 7 minutes.*

The action of the minute repeater is as follows :—

The slide A (Fig. 183) is drawn round and this winds up the repeating mainspring and releases the racks exactly as described when dealing with the best quality quarter repeater. In addition to this action the minute rack B drops under the influence of its spring C so that the tail D contacts a step on the minute snail E. At the same time the pin F, fixed to the winding rack G releases the lever H which is pivoted by a shouldered screw at I. The end of this lever releases the flirt J and allows it to drop a little so as to hold the surprise piece K firmly

146

when no minutes are required to be struck. As the minute rack drops the limb *L* of the pawl *M* contacts the hammer post *N* and holds the pawl out of the path of the six teeth *O*.

The quarter rack is gathered up by the hook shaped piece *P* contacting the pin fixed to rack *Q* and this rack, geared into the internal teeth of the quarter rack, gathers up the quarter rack and at the correct moment the pawl *M* gathers up the minute rack *B* and the teeth *R* contact the hammer pallet *S* and so the minutes are struck.

Oiling

The same technique is employed as with the other repeating watches when oiling (*see* Oiling Chart Fig. 191). Where a light spring is employed, as for the hammer pallet, pawl spring and so on, a light oil is used. Where pressure is applied, as for the lever *H* where it contacts the pin *F* and the pin on the flirt *J*, a heavier oil is used, but in *all* instances the amount of oil used must be small, and as for the quarter repeater, no oil at all should be used on the surprise piece.

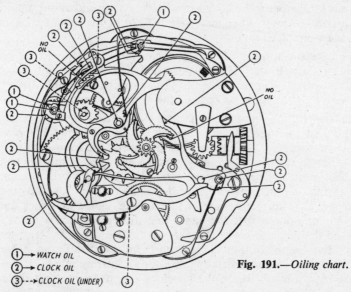

① → WATCH OIL
② → CLOCK OIL
③ --→ CLOCK OIL (UNDER)

Fig. 191.—*Oiling chart.*

Fitting the Hands

The hands are fitted in the following manner :—

Having fitted on the dial (with the movement in its case) turn the hand work until the star wheel has just jumped. Then fit on the hour hand at the hour indicated by the number of hours struck. Place the minute hand on lightly at the exact minute stroke of the dial at

12 o'clock. If the set hands is the pull out type, draw back the repeating slide and hold it firmly (do not allow it to strike). At the same time set the hands and if you hold the watch to your ear you will be able to hear the tail of the minute rack dropping from step to step. Directly you hear the first drop observe the minute hand ; it should be pointing to exactly one minute past the hour. Release the slide and let the striking operate ; in addition to the hours, one minute should strike. If more minutes strike move the minute hand accordingly. Set the hands to exactly quarter past the hour and draw the slide, no minutes should be sounded. Let the watch run normally and just before one minute past the quarter, repeat again—no minutes should be sounded. At exactly one minute past repeat, and one minute should be struck. Try at several stages particularly at the long minutes, 10 to 14, to ensure that they are correct. When you are satisfied, make the minute hand secure.

Repairs

As with the other repeaters, repairs can be a never ending subject. There is little more to be added to what has been said about repairing the quarter repeater other than that the tail of the minute rack may have been tampered with.

The necessity to alter the tail may have been due to wide holes of the centre wheel, etc. Having corrected the original fault, proceed to deal with the tail of the rack. This is done in exactly the same manner as for the quarter rack of the quarter repeater.

The tightness of the cannon pinion is important with all watches, complicated or not, but with five minute and the minute repeaters it is most important. This does not mean that the cannon should be so tight as to endanger the minute wheel teeth when setting the hands, but there must not be any loose spots. If the hand work is loose, the rack falling on to the snail fitted to the cannon could cause the cannon to move. The correct minute or five minute, would be struck and it may not be noticed that the hands had moved forward a minute or two and the timekeeping of the watch may be suspected. It is, therefore, advisable to see that the friction tightness of the cannon pinion is correct and, also to observe the position of the minute hand before the slide is drawn to make the watch repeat, to ensure that the rack falling on to the snail has not moved the minute hand.

Dealing with Gongs

The handling of the gongs is most important. With the majority of repeaters the gongs can be removed before the movement is taken from its case. Remove the two screws holding the gong block to the bottom plate of the movement. Very gently lift the gongs up and

148

away from the movement, holding the gongs by the block with one limb of the tweezers in each of the two screw holes. If the gongs are inclined to stick, on no account use any force but carefully persuade them free. If a gong is fractured, usually near the block, little can be done about it really satisfactorily, the tone is almost sure to suffer a little.

Should a repair be necessary proceed as follows. Drill a hole where the gong fitted in the block, larger than the diameter of the gong wire. Drill the hole as deep as possible, at least 4 to 5 mm. Turn up a piece of brass bushing about 4 mm. long with a hole that fits tightly on to the gong, finally driving it on with a watch hammer to ensure a tight fit. Now file the diameter of the bush by hand until it enters the hole in the block to a depth of, say, 3 mm. tightly.

Fit copper chops on to the bench vice jaws and between these secure the gong block, first heating the end of the block where the hole is until it turns blue (make sure that the other gong is not coloured). While this is hot, press the bushed end of the gong into the hole.

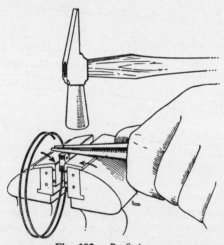

Fig. 192.—Re-fitting a gong.

Make sure that the gong is in its correct position, the other gong fitted to it will act as a guide. Then with a pair of stout brass tweezers straddle the gong, as in Fig. 192, tap the bush on the gong until all the brass bush has disappeared into the hole. Tap the tweezers as near the gong as possible.

Should the block be too hard to drill, let the end down to a blue, and do not forget to take precautions against colouring the other gong. After drilling, remove the blue from the side of the block with an emery buff as this white surface will be required as a guide to the heating when driving the gong into position.

After heating the block, the fitting must be done quickly as the expansion of the block is being employed to ensure a tight grip on the bushed end as the block cools and contracts. Remove from the vice and allow to cool. Remove the blue from the block as explained in " Practical Watch Repairing." If care has been taken with the positioning of the gong on the block, the gong will lie parallel to the bottom plate when screwed in position. It is never advisable to attempt to solder a gong. The heat running along the gong will reduce its hardness and deaden its tone.

A. *Days of the week dial.*
B. *Date of the month dial.*
C. *Seconds hand.*
D. *Month of the year dial.*
E. *Phases of the moon dial.*
F. *Chronograph hand.*
G. *Chronograph minute counter hand.*
H. *Chronograph push.*
I. *Repeating slide.*

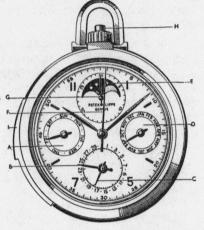

Fig. 193.—*Dial of a triple complicated watch.*

Triple Complicated Watch

The triple complicated watch has these three complications:–

1. Chronograph.
2. Calendar.
3. Repeater.

The calendar mechanism may be the perpetual system and the repeating mechanism the minute repeater, or the calendar may be the 31-day system where the first of the month must be changed manually if there are less than 31 days in the previous month. The repeater can be the simple quarter repeater. The watch illustrated in Fig. 193 is the perpetual calendar with minute repeater and chronograph. Some such watches are fitted with split seconds chronographs and some, much more rare, with clock watch mechanism.

Usually the chronograph mechanism is fitted to the top plate and repeating work mounted on to the bottom plate in the conventional manner. The perpetual calendar work is mounted on to a separate plate which is screwed to the movement over the repeating work. The best advice that can be given to the craftsman about to overhaul such a watch is CARE. All that has already been said about *utmost care* applies with greater force still.

The repair of a triple complicated watch should not be undertaken by any person who is not *fully proficient* with repeaters, perpetual calendars and chronographs. There must always be a " first time " but to tackle such a watch unless you are fully conversant with the function of each of the three complications is, to say the least, foolhardy.

Clock Watches

Clock watches strike the hours and the quarters automatically as the watch goes, similar to a ting-tang striking clock. Like the clock,

150

most clock watches are fitted with two trains, one for the striking and one for the going and repeating. A lever is provided in the form of a small repeating slide, but it cannot be drawn round. It just operates another lever which releases the strike train so that the watch will then strike the hours, quarters and the minutes as an ordinary minute repeater.

Some clock watches are $\frac{1}{4}$ repeaters only. With all clock watches the mainspring of the repeating is not wound by drawing the slide when using the watch as a repeater. The spring is wound once each day ; the forward movement of the winding button winds the going train, and the backward movement the striking and repeating train. In the case of a keywound clock watch there are two squares to wind.

The action of the clock watch is as follows. The movement being described here is a very fine example of English work. It will be noticed that the striking barrel A (Fig. 194) is larger than the going barrel B, the reason being that the striking will require a longer running time than the going side since, if the watch is set at " full

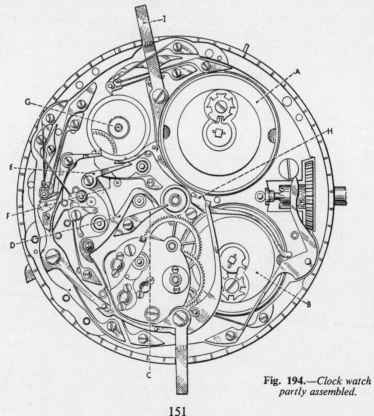

Fig. 194.—*Clock watch partly assembled.*

strike " it will strike the hours and quarters at each quarter of an hour and, in addition, there must be a reserve of power to operate when the slide is released because the repeating work is required, say, 12 or even more times in the 24 hours.

The cannon pinion (Fig. 195) has fitted to its underside a four-star wheel and as it rotates it contacts, at each quarter of an hour, the lever *C* (Fig. 194), which in turn lifts the lever *D*. Fitted on to this lever is the lever *E*, which is free to move, being held by a shouldered screw, and held in the forward position by the spring *F*. Gearing into the barrel *A* is an intermediate wheel which in turn gears into the wheel with a long, extended squared arbor *G*, and on this arbor is fitted the wheel assembly (Fig. 196). This consists of a steel disc with a long pipe with a square hole. Fitted to the underside of this disc is a steel ratchet wheel with a round hole(Fig. 197). This is free to move, but the extent of its movement is controlled by the two screws *D* and *E*, which also hold it in position. *A* is the rivet of the pin *A* as shown in Fig. 196. When this assembly is in position the nose of the lever *E* (Fig. 194) contacts the ratchet teeth and, as the cannon pinion rotates, the ratchet wheel is stepped forward one tooth. Fixed to the ratchet wheel is a pin *A* (Figs. 196 and 197), which projects through a large hole in the steel disc and when the ratchet wheel is moved forward this pin contacts the click *B* (Fig. 196). The click is held so that its nose is pressed toward the centre by the spring *C*. While the movement is in its present state of assembly we will go back a little.

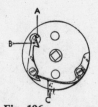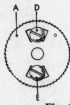

Fig. 195.—*Cannon pinion of clock watch.*

Fig. 196
Fig. 197
Wheel assembly which is the driving unit of the clock watch.

When setting the hands, the lever *H* (Fig. 194) is automatically moved so that the lever *E* is held out of action and therefore the striking train is not released. If it were not for this lever the striking train would be released when the hands were set, thus causing an unnecessary waste of power. Also, when it is required not to use the striking part at all, the lever *I*, is moved to the right and the lever *E* is held away from the teeth of the ratchet wheel, but this does not prevent the repeating from operating.

To resume. Fitted on to the pipe of the disc (Fig. 196) is the wheel assembly *A* (Fig. 198) which consists of a ratchet wheel on to which is screwed the hour rack *B*. On to this rack is screwed the pinion *C* which gears with the rack *D*. This last-mentioned wheel assembly has a round hole so that it is free to rotate backward and forward. The end of the rack is the tail *E* which, when the rack is released, contacts the snail *F*, and so the number of the hours to be struck is controlled. Since the disc (Fig. 196) is—as far as the assembly has progressed—the only component with a square hole, it is this disc, through its click *B*, which is the motive force to the clock watch part of the mechanism.

As the squared arbor rotates in an anti-clockwise direction the nose of the click *B* (Fig. 196) draws round with it the wheel assembly *A* (Fig. 198).

On the squared arbor is fitted the rack *A* (Fig. 200) which has a round hole fitting on to the pipe of the gathering pallet *B*, which has a square hole. The gathering pallet *B* contacts the pin *C* fixed to the rack *A* which gears into the teeth of the minute rack *D*. From here the action is exactly similar to the minute repeating mechanism as already explained. Upon completion of the striking, the end of the

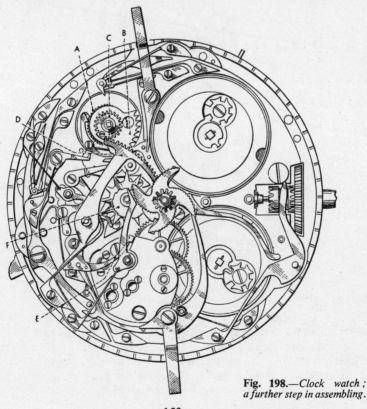

Fig. 198.—*Clock watch ; a further step in assembling.*

minute rack contacts the pin E fixed to the lever F and a pin at the other end of this lever is brought into the path of the pallets of the striking train and stops it. The lever G (Fig. 200) is to release the striking train when it is required to use the watch as a repeater. The lever H, if moved to the left, causes the watch to strike the quarters only and to the right for full strike. Under the minute wheel and fixed to the minute-wheel pinion is a 3-star wheel A (Fig. 199). The cannon pinion is of 12 leaves and the minute wheel 36 teeth ; there-fore, at each quarter-hour one of the teeth of the star wheel lifts the lever B so that if the lever C is placed to " quarters only " the watch will strike hours and quarters at the hour ; since there are only three teeth to the star wheel the lever B will not be lifted at the hour. The cannon pinion and minute wheel are marked so as to ensure that the star wheel is in the correct position.

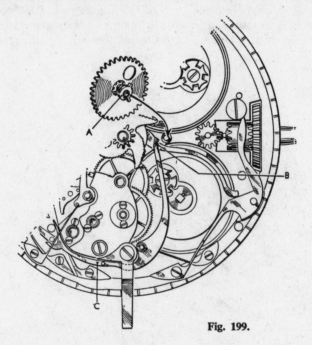

Fig. 199.

Oiling

The instructions given when referring to oiling repeating watches applies here to clock watches. Lightly oil with watch oil parts with little or no force behind them and with clock oil parts where pressure is likely to be too great for watch oil to withstand. The correct oiling of such watches as these can only be the result of experience, and a good deal of experience at repairing repeating watches first.

General Notes

The same remarks as were made when dealing with repeating watches apply to fitting the hands of clock watches.

As with repeating watches, it would be practically impossible to enumerate the repairs that may be necessary. One *must* depend upon experience and the best possible advice that can be given is that if you have not a good experience of minute repeaters do not attempt clock watches.

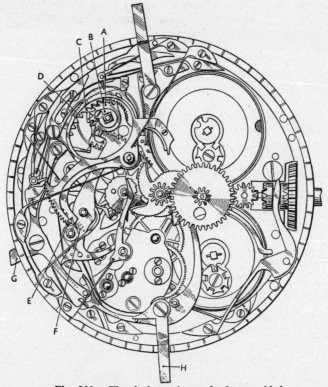

Fig. 200.—*The clock watch completely assembled.*

The clock watch illustrated and described here is one of the finest examples the writer has had the pleasure of examining. It is of English manufacture and there is every indication that the clock watch mechanism is English also. Many repeating watches are to be found where the movement as a whole is English, but the repeating train, etc., is Swiss. The movements were sent to Switzerland for this work to be done and then returned to England for completion as watches.

Some clock watches are made to repeat the hours and quarters only—no minutes. Others, to lower the cost of manufacture, are made with the clock watch train running from the going train barrel ; there is only one barrel.

Very few clock watches are made at the present time other than to special order. Other than as a novelty or an exhibition of crafts-manship, they serve no useful purpose. The cost of repairing such watches is relatively high and demands a high standard of workman-ship and to see a surfeit of clock watches passing through the repair workshops could, under existing conditions, be embarrassing.

Section 8

INDEPENDENT AND JUMPING SECONDS WATCHES

Independent Seconds

Independent seconds watches are provided with two mainsprings and two separate trains. The time of day train terminates with an escapement and the other with a flirt fitted to a pinion, the flirt is usually of two arms and made of gold. The arms are of such a length that they engage in the leaves of the escape-wheel pinion. When one arm is released from a leaf of the pinion the other flies round and is arrested by the next leaf. The independent train is so calculated that a half-turn of the flirt pinion allows the wheel, to which the seconds hand is fitted to its pinion, to advance one-sixtieth of a turn and so records one second. The hand advances by dead beats. The independent seconds can be centre seconds or off-set.

In an 18000 train with a 15-tooth escape wheel the pinion upon which the flirt acts has six leaves, since the wheel rotates once in six seconds, i.e. the pinion must have as many leaves as the escape wheel occupies seconds in making one rotation.

Usually a slide is fitted to the side of the case which operates a lever to stop the flirt when the independent seconds is not required ; stopping the flirt does not stop the watch.

Some trains are so calculated that the independent seconds hand jumps 15 seconds, i.e. four beats to the minute.

The arms of the flirt engaging in the pinion are not oiled. The only other point to note is to see that the seconds hand is so placed in position that it drops exactly on to the seconds mark and that it fits on to its pivot tightly. The continued jerking of the hand as it jumps each second can loosen it.

Jumping Seconds

A seconds recording centre-seconds watch is made by Lovary, Ltd., Le Locle, Switzerland, known as the " jumping seconds " watch. The effect is similar to the independent-seconds watch and its purpose is to meet the demand for a watch where an indication of complete seconds is required from a running hand. A chronograph or timer will record fractions of a second, and the average centre-seconds hand records 1/5th second, but it is not possible to read fifths of a second with a running seconds hand.

157

In the Lovary watch this complete seconds jump serves a useful purpose ; a single second can be read accurately. For instance, starting races where a certain number of seconds handicap or interval is to be determined can be done accurately with this watch, which is much less expensive than a chronograph.

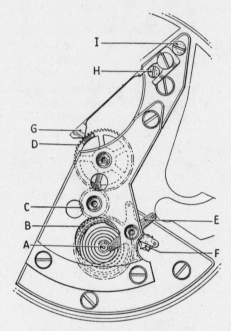

Fig. 201.—*Plan of Lovary watch.*

The movement is well made and its construction most ingenious and simple. Its action is as follows : Fig. 201 is a plan view and Fig. 202 an exploded view with the bridge of the centre work removed. Fitted to the extended pivot of the fourth wheel is a balance spring, collet *A*, to which is pinned a balance spring. The wheel *B* is recessed on the inside of the outer edge and is supported by the balance spring. The outer end of the balance spring is not attached to the wheel, so the spring can slip if prolonged obstruction is placed upon the wheel, such as caused by the hands catching. The wheel *B* gears into a steel intermediate wheel *C* which in turn gears into the centre-seconds wheel *D*. A pinion, fixed to the six-star wheel *E*, also gears into the wheel *B*. Pins are fitted to the star wheel and they contact the six-star wheel *F*, which is fitted friction-tight on to the extended pivot of the escape wheel.

158

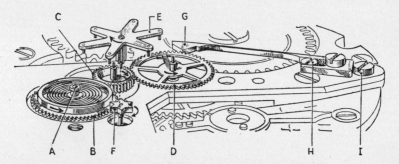

Fig. 202.—*The Lovary watch with centre work removed.*

As the fourth wheel rotates it carries with it the balance spring and therefore the wheel *B* by virtue of the tension of the spring. The star wheel *E* rotates, but its progress is checked by the pins contacting the teeth of the star wheel *F* which allows the star wheel *E* to jump at one-second intervals. The balance spring is wound up slightly before each jump. The seconds jumps are transmitted to the wheel *D* to which the seconds hand is fitted. The wheel *D* is controlled by the jumper spring *G* and this is adjusted for tension by an eccentric screw-head *H*. The position of the seconds hand is adjusted by an eccentric screw-head *I*, so as to ensure that the seconds hand points to a seconds mark.

A refinement is that when the winding button is at set hands, the watch is stopped so that the seconds hand can be set accurately.

Section 9

MORE AUTOMATIC WATCHES

Since the first section of this book was written and the drawings prepared, a number of other automatic watch calibres have appeared on the market, proving that this type of movement is rapidly gaining in popularity.

In order to make the book as up-to-date as possible, a selection of these movements is described and illustrated and their repair considered in this and the following pages.

ALPINA

Made by Alpina Union Horlogère S.A., Bienne, Switzerland (Fig. 203) the Alpina movement is 10½''', the oscillating weight turning

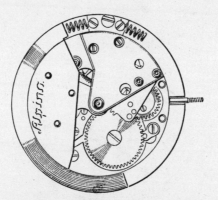

Fig. 203.—*The movement and its winding weight.*

through a segment of a circle and being controlled by two buffer springs, *A* (Fig. 204). The mainspring is wound as the rotor swings in one direction only. The automatic mechanism is quite simple and consists of three parts only, the rotor *B* with a pinion fixed to it, which gears into the rack *C*. A click with spring contacts the fine-toothed ratchet wheel *D*, which has a pinion fixed to it. This pinion gears into the transmission wheel of the normal keyless work. The arrangement is ingenious and efficient.

161

To dismantle.—Remove the two screws *E*, *F*, and lift the plate off. This releases the rotor, rack, and the fine-toothed ratchet wheel.

Oiling.—The manufacturers recommend that the pivots of the three parts—the rotor, rack and fine-toothed ratchet wheel—be oiled with good quality clock oil. The ratchet teeth and the click screw with watch oil.

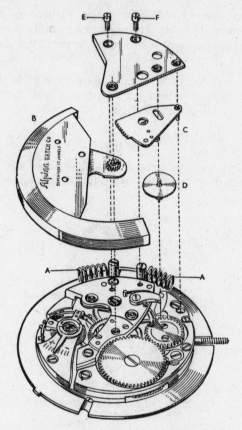

Fig. 204.—*Dismantling of automatic winding work.*

During assembly, arrange so that the tooth on the edge of the rack engages the leaves of the pinion fixed to the rotor when the rotor is bearing against the right-hand buffer spring *A*, this ensures that the fullest advantage is taken of the movement of the rotor. Apply test given on page 5.

AVIA

The Avia Automatic is made by Degoumois and Co., Neuchâtel, Switzerland, who use the ebauche of A. Schild S.A., of Grenchen, Switzerland. This movement is fully described *on page 57* and is named by Schild, Rotomatic.

It may be repeated here that the ebauche, or frame, is made by the ebauche manufacturer who supplies it to the finisher, as in this instance, and they have the escapement made, fit the jewel holes, finish the plates and bridges, and spring and time it, all to their own standard of quality. Finally the dial and hands are fitted and the case supplied and the completed watch is marketed by the finisher. Quite rightly, the finisher is the manufacturer, since he determines the quality of the finish of the movement and is responsible for the production of the completed watch.

BUREN ROTOWIND

The Buren Rotowind, made by the Buren Watch Co., Buren a/A, Switzerland (Fig. 205) is produced in two sizes of movement, $9\frac{1}{4}'''$ and $11\frac{1}{2}'''$. Both calibres are fitted with up and down—reserve power

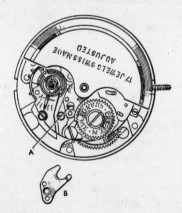

Fig. 205.—*The Rotowind movement.*

—indicators and the construction of each is exactly similar. The rotor rotates the full 360° and winds in both directions. A pinion fixed to the rotor engages the wheel *A* (Fig. 206) the pinion of which in turn gears into the wheel *B*. The wheel *B* gears into one or the other of the reverser wheels *C*, and these wheels gear into a pinion which winds the mainspring through the transmission wheel of the normal keyless work.

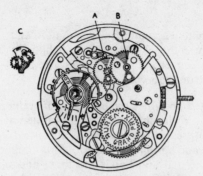

Fig. 206.—*Buren movement without automatic winding work.*

To dismantle.—Remove the screw *A* (Fig. 205) and draw away the rotor fixing plate *B*. To let the mainspring down release the click of the wheel *A* (Fig. 206) and let the spring down in the normal manner.

Oiling.—The manufacturers give special instructions as regards oiling. The pivots of the automatic train are oiled with watch oil, the rotor bearing with clock oil. No oil is applied to the pivot or bearing of the reverser plate, this must be perfectly free and any oil would tend to cause it to stick. No oil is applied to the teeth, or beak of the click, of the wheel *A* (Fig. 206) or to the bearing of the click. Apply test as page 5.

CYMA

The Cyma automatic is made by the Cyma Watch Co., La Chaux-de-Fonds, Switzerland. The basic movement is $8\frac{3}{4}'''$, with the weight it is $11'''$ (Fig. 207). The oscillating weight turns a segment of a circle and is controlled by two buffer springs. The mainspring is wound as the rotor swings in one direction only. The automatic mechanism is quite simple, and well designed. The click *A* (Fig. 208) engages the wheel *B*, which gears into the wheel *C*. This wheel has a pinion fixed to it which gears into the wheel *D* and the pinion of this wheel gears into the ratchet wheel *E* and so winds the mainspring.

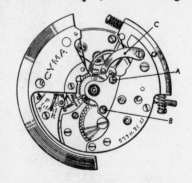

Fig. 207.—*Cyma movement with oscillating weight.*

To dismantle.—Remove the screws *A* and *B* (Fig. 207) and lift the plate which holds the rotor in position. The remaining dismantling

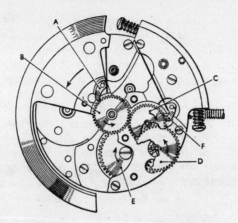

Fig. 208.—*Action of automatic winding.*

is clear. The bar with pin projecting, *C*, is to hold the movement firmly in its case ; the back of the case screws on to it.

Oiling.—The manufacturers advise oiling the pivots of the automatic train with Chronax S. See page 4. No oil should be applied to the beak of the stop click *E*, but a little watch oil to the stud only. Finally apply test *as given on page 5.*

ETERNA-MATIC

The Eterna Watch Co., Grenchen, Switzerland, make several calibres from $7\frac{3}{4}'''$ to $13\frac{1}{2}'''$ with centre seconds and off-set seconds. The

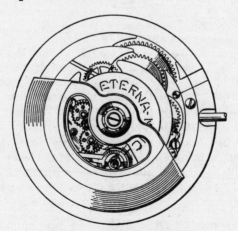

Fig. 209.—*The Eterna-matic.*

165

principle of all the calibres is the same (Fig. 209). The rotor rotates the full 360° and it winds the mainspring in both directions. The rotor is fitted with a ball race of five ball bearings. This movement is among the flattest automatic winding watches made. Fixed to the rotor is the wheel *A* (Fig. 210) which gears with two reverser wheels *B, C*. A similar reverser wheel is described on page 17. The direction of drive of the under wheel of one differs from that of the other ; therefore, as the rotor rotates in the direction of arrow, the wheel *B* will drive—and in the other direction the wheel *C* will drive. Both the under wheels gear together but the top wheels are separated. The pinion of the under wheel of *C* gears with another wheel, which is thus made to rotate always in the same direction and so, through a train of wheels to the ratchet wheel, to wind the mainspring.

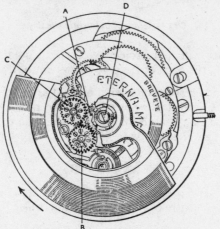

Fig. 210.—*Action of the automatic winding.*

To dismantle.—The screw *D* is removed ; the rotor can then be lifted off. To fit a new mainspring, the whole of the automatic mechanism can be removed *en bloc*. The manufacturers advise that the ball race is not removed and that the reverser wheel is not taken to pieces. If either of these parts is found to be faulty it should be the watch is fully assembled apply the test as given on page 5.

Oiling.—The ball bearings are very sparingly oiled with watch oil. No oil at all should be applied to the clicks of the reverser wheel, but the pivots of the wheel itself are oiled with a little watch oil. When the watch is fully assembled apply the test as given on page 5.

OMEGA

The Omega Watch Co. have added two new automatic winding watches to their range. They are the Calibre 455 ladies' model and calibres 471 and 501 gentlemen's models (471—25.50 mm. diameter and 501—28.50 mm. diameter). Other than the diameter the calibres are identical.

In calibre 455 (Fig. 211) the rotor rotates through 360° and it winds in both directions. Fixed to the underside of the rotor is a disc with

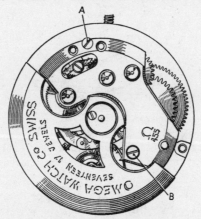

Fig. 211.—*Omega automatic calibre* 455

three teeth and three pins (Fig. 213) which gear alternately into the three teeth on each side of the rocking arm *A* which is pivoted at *B*.

Fitted on to an arm are two clicks *C* and *D* and these clicks contact the wheels *A* and *B* (Fig. 212) so that as the arm rocks in either direction

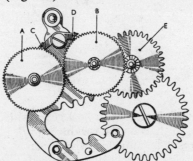

Fig. 212.—*The automatic winding system of calibre* 455.

the wheel *B* will always rotate clockwise, either because of the direct push of the click *D* as the arm rocks to the right or the teeth of the wheel *A* as the arm rocks to the left. The pinion of the wheel *B* gears into the wheel *E* and its pinion gears into the ratchet wheel and so winds the mainspring, a most ingenious, simple and sturdy device.

167

It is important that the assembly of the rocking arm shall be arranged as in Fig. 213 for the correct operating of the automatic mechanism.

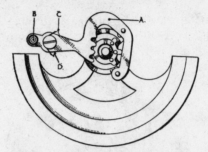

Fig. 213.—*Underside of the rotor.*

The whole of the automatic work can be removed complete by removing the two screws *A* and *B* (Fig. 211), when the carriage carrying the mechanism is lifted off.

In calibres 471 and 501 (Fig. 215) the rotor rotates 360° and winds in both directions. Fixed to the rotor is the wheel *A* (Fig. 214) which

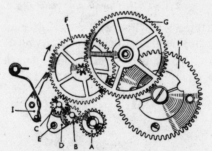

Fig. 214.—*Automatic winding mechanism of Omega calibre 471.*

gears into the wheel *B* and this wheel gears with the wheel *C* which are both fitted on to studs on the rocking arm *D*, pivoted at *E*. When the wheel *A* rotates in an anti-clockwise direction, the wheel *C* is made to gear with the wheel *F* which thus rotates in a clockwise direction, and, as the rotor reverses, the wheel *A* rotates in a clockwise direction, and the wheel *B* will gear with the wheel *F* direct, which will still rotate in a clockwise direction. The pinion of the wheel *F* gears with the wheel *G* and its pinion gears into the ratchet wheel *H* and so winds the mainspring. The click *I* holds up the mainspring until the main click takes over. The ratchet work of the main ratchet wheel is contained in a special assembly of the wheel itself.

This movement is of exceptionally good design and is very robust. The whole of the automatic mechanism can be removed *en bloc* by removing the two screws A and B (Fig. 215).

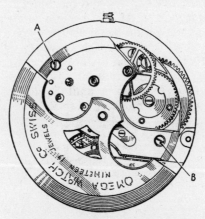

Fig. 215.—*The automatic mechanism is removed by taking out the screws A and B.*

Both the ladies' and gentlemen's movements are fitted with dual indexes, so that the final adjustment can be effected with the normal index.   In addition, the larger model is fitted with a micrometer adjustment to the index.

Omega recommend Syntalube oil for oiling the automatic mechanism of both movements.   Apply test as noted on page 5.

ROAMER ROTOPOWER
Made by the Roamer Watch Co. S.A., Soleure, Switzerland (Fig. 216) the Rotopower has a rotor that turns the full 360° and winds the main-

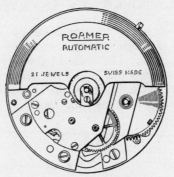

Fig. 216.—*Roamer movement with 260° winding.*

spring in both directions. Fixed to the rotor is the wheel A (Fig. 217) which gears into the wheel B. Both wheels B and C are free to rotate on studs fixed on to a rocking bar. As the rotor travels in the direction of the arrow, the wheel C gears into the wheel D. When the rotor reverses its motion, the wheel B gears into the wheel D. Thus the wheel D always rotates in the same direction, as arrow.

The pinion of wheel D gears into the wheel E and the pinion of this wheel gears into wheel F which in turn gears direct into the ratchet wheel and so the mainspring is wound. The stop click G controls the wheel D and holds the train up until the click of the ratchet wheel takes over. Apply test as noted on page 5.

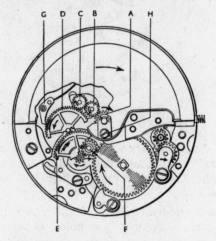

Fig. 217.—*Action of the movement.*

To dismantle.—The screw H is removed and the plate holding the rotor in position is withdrawn. The rotor is then lifted off.

Oiling.—The pivots of the automatic train are oiled with Chronax H oil (*see page* 4). The manufacturers recommend that all parts needing oil are oiled lightly. The studs of the two reverser wheels are just greased with a greasy pegwood charged with Chronax H oil and the same treatment to the pivots of the stop click G. If an oiler is used in the conventional manner, too much oil will be applied.

ROTARY

The Rotary Automatic is made by Moise Dreyfuss, La Chaux-de-Fonds, Switzerland. This factory uses the ebauche made by A. Schild, Cal. 1488. The calibre is fitted, however, with a reserve power indicator—up and down work. Other than that, the system is as explained on pages 57-59. As mentioned before, the rough ebauche is finished to the standard of quality of the factory using it. In this case Messrs. Dreyfuss control the quality of the escapement used, also they fit the jewel holes, mainspring, balance spring and time and regulate the watch. Finally they fit the dial and hands, supply the case and market the finished watch. This factory is responsible for the completed watch.

INDEX